Arlene

All My Love -

TALK
TO GOD

The Experts in Publishing   *   *New York*

The book that changes
your thoughts about
God, the universe,
everything.

TALK TO GOD

From the Breakout
Author...

DeiAmor
Verus

EIP

PUBLISHED BY THE EXPERTS IN PUBLISHING, INC

Copyright © DeiAmor Verus, LLC

All Rights Reserved

Published in the United States by The Experts in Publishing, Inc.
New York
www.theexpertsinpublishing.com

EXPERTS IN PUBLISHING and its logo, a letter E on a right angle, are trademarks of The Experts in Publishing, Inc.

Book design by Experts in Publishing

ISBN 978-0-9890122-0-1

PRINTED IN THE UNITED STATES OF AMERICA

10 9 8 7 6 5 4 3

To Joseph, Nicholas, Jacob & Monica.
I hear you in my dreams mom.

Table of Contents

PROLOGUE

8

You want me to talk to God? I'll talk to God!
I'll send you to Him you motherfucker! Here I am!

9

Where are you going? You are alone.
You have nowhere to go and no one to go home to.
You eat alone; you sleep alone; you have nothing.
Your wife is gone.

10

Usually that's the second question asked,
number one is: Is there a heaven?

11

Hold on! I like the God has a plan thing.
Not true, but I like it.

12

Can you have lost your mind and still evaluate
your present mental stability to determine
if you lost your mind. What the fuck am I talking about?

13

Do you listen to my prayers, to everyone's prayers?

14

The cure for an individual's cancer
is inside each and every one of you.

15

There is an odd sensation of contentment
when you start believing the homeless person you are talking
to is truly God. Does that sound odd to anyone else?

16

I shouted, "THIS IS GOD!"

17

"No: Though shall not kill, mess around with another man's wife,
Though shall not steal -none of that?"

18

Just kidding. Good Question. Good news:
You're talking to the person named Jesus Christ right now.

19

"Did you know you were going to be killed that night
in front of the Dakota Apartment in New York?"

20

"Find a child who is abused, beaten and tortured
and hug them and feel the wealth of unused love
swell from their souls into yours."

21

"I went there one Sunday and told them I was God.
They gave me water, five dollars, a pamphlet on drug addiction
and escorted me out."

22

We are children, no, worse: we are child bullies
in a world that requires unconditional love. Fuck.

23

They brainwash the masses with horrible
stories about God and my wrath.
I don't have any wrath.

24

On the seventh day I rested was also a whopper.
It was written that way to make sure people showed up for church
instead of boozing and ass grabbing.

25

"The Old Testament is a book of fiction written by frightened charlatans
just trying to keep the masses in line."

26

That is what humans will evolve to. That is your afterlife.
That is your heaven - and I haven't had one complaint.

27

Gabriel says to Mohammad,
"All the teachings of Moses and Jesus are incorrect."
I guess that part is close to the truth but I digress.

28

Truth be told, I thought I looked a lot like Jay Z
when I was on earth with the name Jesus.

29

But let's back up to a little time before the Big Bang.

30

I guess to them you are aliens.

31

Take him now, or they will kill him right here
right now, and they will not stop com —

32

Religious people? Religious people want to kill you?

33

You don't know how hungry you are until stale rolls
at Denny's start looking really good to you.

34

He looks at me and sees optimism through my hollowed out,
reddened eyes, barely attached anymore to
what's left of my broken heart.

35

Who stands outside the abortion clinic when those
children come out - broken, sad, lost, full of inconsolable guilt?
Who? Who hugs them? Who loves them? I DO!

36

We arrive at my apartment: a cheap, stucco, 14 unit
Dumpster with no common amenities, just 14 doors,
opening to 14 sad stories - eight hundred square feet of loneliness.

37

God gets to his feet and stretches.
You hear bones cracking, farting.
He then rolls his neck until he gets it to crack.

38

Oh my God! Oh my God! You really are bleeding!
Stop it! You can stop it!
You can do anything! Fucking stop it!

EPOLOGUE

Your life changes when you spend a weekend with God.

PROLOGUE

I never wrote a book. I am not an author. I can barely string a few sentences together in an email. So if you are looking for Hemingway or Steinbeck you're fucked.

I really don't care what you think of me but you and everyone else should know the truth about love, life and what happens after you die. You may be compelled to ask, how would I know what happens afterwards? If I answer that question truthfully you will, like he said you will, lump me in the same pile of lunatic shit brains, religious freaks, and holy fucking rollers. I am none of those. I am a regular guy, who lost his wife to cancer. I know pain.

If you had to spend a weekend with the creator of the universe what would you ask him or her? I did, and if you think you are going hear me spew page after page about heaven, angels, pearly gates, divine order, prayers, and reflect on Biblical passages you are gravely wrong. In fact God doesn't think much of the Bible and more surprisingly he thinks religion is horse shit.

I think what will startle most people after reading this is that the science guys, the atheists and agnostics, are closer to the truth about the universe and the afterlife than the religions. And that's straight from God's lips to my ears with one very unique caveat that will blow your mind.

He told me if I wrote anything down, not to lie, don't make shit up or stretch the truth like they did in the Bible. I haven't. He also said I would be treated like shit for writing this. I thought about it a long time before I did. But it's too important not to share.

If you are interested in knowing the truth about, well about everything, turn the page. If not, fuck it, throw the book away.

TALK
TO GOD

1

*"There's is a numbing that occurs when
you are watching someone you love slowly die."*

There's is a numbing that occurs when you are watching
someone you love slowly die. It begins as a violently sickening
pain. Then hope is trampled ever so slowly by the realization that
there is no salvation, no cure, not even an outside chance of a
miracle. And that is when the numbing begins.

People who know you, that are around you, describe you
as strong, stoic, when actually the levels of pain and every
direction it comes continually hardens the numbness. You are not
strong or stoic: Your mind has shut down those senses to feel, to
love in a feeble attempt to preserve you from walking off a cliff.
Things that make me cry now are no longer my wife's sullen,
lonely eyes, or my staring into them reminiscing about younger,
healthier times. But instead I cry hysterically, alone, when I walk
past the dust covered kitchen table where no one has sat since she
went into the hospital for the last time.

Oh, the Sunday mornings. We were hip deep in "us."
We brewed our favorite coffee, not the weekday instant crap
because we were rushing to work, but the kind that smelled like
freshly ground coffee beans, our legs entangled under the table,
gently tickling each other in our favorite spots. Those eyes
meeting in silent glances that shouted, "We are madly in love."

And the smell of her perfume from the night before mixed with the fabric softener in her robe and her skin, oh her wonderful, angel-like skin. Her aroma was my pure joy, indescribable bliss. If true love had an aroma it was that for me. I miss that smell the most.

I cry hardest when I awake in the mornings. The switch that lets you fall asleep and forget does not switch on the moment you awake. There is a five-second delay when your mind hasn't separated your dreams from the reality of the day's upcoming pain. But as soon as you get your bearings it crushes you. The pain presses down on you, suffocating and merciless. This pain does not allow one to be strong nor stoic. I have found the morning assault of pain - when I remember how hopeless life has become - is the most violent, the most destructive.

I sleep in a chair. I have not the mental strength to sleep in "our" bed because it is "our" bed. I stare at it. Alone, cold, flat, made, tucked marine tight the way she made it every morning. The way she made it the day she left. I know that neither she nor I will ever sleep in our bed again. I never thought an un-slept-in bed could look so lonely.
There is no numbness in the morning, just tears, wailing, hateful tears. You start moving toward the bathroom to brush your teeth just to wash the bile out of the back of your mouth to avoid vomiting. It works about half the time. From the moment I awake to the 30 seconds to the bathroom I have already become mentally and physically exhausted.

I move through the ordeal of getting showered and dressed without a concern as to clothing or hygiene. Three day old underwear, un-pressed shirts, in need of a haircut, and I don't care. This was her thing. Everything was always clean and in its place. Now nothing is right. Nothing is in its place. Everything around me reminds me of her. This place is her. Now our home has become my hollow, mental torture chamber. The place we built and loved? I hate it more than I despise the hospital. Something that no one ever tells you when the person you love is dying is that all the great memories, the photos, videos, scrapbooks and mementos that you took the time to preserve so no moment would ever be forgotten, become bullets in a gun firing through my brain. You pray to God you could forget. And it's not just the pictures or mementos. It's the coffee cup I use that she bought me on my birthday. It's the drapes and furniture we picked out, the appliances she said would match – they didn't - the paint color in every room. And her smell is everywhere. Tell me that someday I will want to keep these memories, but right now I wish they would disappear.

I try to keep up appearances at work. All the sick days are gone, the vacation days used, but they understand and have been sympathetic. I think it is easier for them to allow me to come and go as I please so they don't have to ask me; "How's it going?" Sympathy? I never wanted it, never thought I would need it. I just hope they put up with it all a little while longer and that the insurance company doesn't stop paying the mountain of bills. My job isn't that important. We both had jobs that didn't require overtime or sacrifice. Working just afforded us a means to an end, and that end was us together every evening and weekend. Inseparable would be a pale description of our relationship. Now I find myself sitting at my desk in a trancelike state. What's really strange when I am at work? I am not crying or consumed with our past memories. I am not thinking about work or chemotherapy, the news on the radio, or the latest office scuttlebutt. I have physically and mentally shut down. I can feel drool cresting on the edge of my mouth, about to run down my cheek, and I don't care. It's like I stepped off the planet, shut down all human functions and am watching the world in a frozen state of animation where I can see what's going on around me, but I can't or don't want to speak or move. I have been wrapped in cellophane and placed on the discard pile of life.

Remember friends? I don't. Another fatality that occurs when someone you love is dying is that your "friends" disappear. They start out with good intentions. The flowers, a casserole, maybe a hospital visit or two, but when the body begins to decompose while the person is still breathing like it does with cancer, it's hard for people to witness. I don't blame them. No one should have to live through the extended methadone drip of someone they love dying unless they love them so much they

3

would pray to trade places with them in a heartbeat like I do every morning.

It is better that friends are not around. I, too, am not myself any longer. I fear I would say something hateful, swing the uncomfortable hospital chair at them, the chair I now live in eight hours a day. Or cuss them out for not being here more often. I am a fountain of pain and it would be no trouble to rain down on them the hate that lives in my soul. Cancer doesn't just kill the patient. I am now collateral damage. I am sure I will see them all again at the funeral. I am sure I won't feel like throwing chairs there.

I thought I reached the most pain a human being could swallow, until one day as I was sitting in my uncomfortable chair at the hospital my bride awoke to tell me it was important for her to plan her own funeral.

Our eyes have cried a sea of tears over the last eight months, but this I couldn't take. Like the secretary at one of her charity organizations, I am supposed to sit there, take notes, and author her obituary; I couldn't bear the thought of doing it. I just dropped my head into my hands and started to wail. After a moment I noticed something was missing from "our" vigil: her. I looked up, shirt soaked with my tears, and saw my wife calmly waiting for me to finish. She seemed in control, at peace, and on task.

This was so her - I mean the healthy her. Everything had to be just her way. This was no exception. It was the first time I told her "NO!" over the last eight months. I immediately jumped into the broken record stuff that I had been saying; "don't talk like that babe – we're gonna beat this," "stay positive, keep fighting." She smirked with a "who's kidding who," look followed by a sarcastic wheeze.

There was no winning this argument, either. I tried. Like a child refusing to go to bed, I stood up and raised my voice "I am sorry, but this time you are going to have to let this one chore, this one job, this one final family party get taken care of by Mr.

Forgot the Potato Salad!" Then another look, the "you are full of shit" look, then she kept moving past me, as she always did and continued to bark items on the list down to the guest list. I didn't know you could make a guest list for a funeral, but there in my lap was the guest list to her funeral.

There was no stopping her once she found something that was important to her to do. She determined where the memorial service should be held; she was donating her body to the medical department at her alma mater so I have been spared the joy of choosing a wig for her or what music to play, or who should speak, or the type of flowers. And she made me swear that her mother, who is nearly blind, got a good seat in front. As I scribbled furiously, something dawned on me: She had accepted her fate and she wanted to do what she loved to do, which was to plan things. And the only thing left was to plan her own funeral. I don't know at what moment it happened, but sometime last night, when they kicked me out of her room for snoring too loudly, and when I came back from the waiting room in the early morning, she must have had a moment of clarity or submission or maybe just exhaustion, but there was an aura of peace about her. Had she mentally succumbed? Was she just waiting for her body to catch up? Always in charge, always right–even now. So what better thing to do with her time than to plan the last thing she was going to do: die.

If you don't have someone in your life who likes to "handle things," find one. They are amazing, and at times, a real pain in the ass. Efficient as a NASA computer. Birthdays of obscure relatives, Christmas cards, people's names at parties, she never missed one. She knew everybody's spouse's names–even the catty, bitches she didn't like, or especially those.
Never forgot a gift or one thing at the grocery store. It was like living with a human Rolodex. She worked as many hours at her job as I did and still kept the house immaculately clean. Where did she find the time? Forget about dirty clothes or dishes in the sink or dust: I didn't even know what those things looked like after a while.

I didn't even know how socially inept I was until I met her. She smoothed the edges of my life. She was the calm in all my storms. She taught me about good scotch, great wine, dining out instead of going out to eat, what a good tie was supposed to look like and how to tie a half Windsor. She taught me to relax, to laugh loudly, to sing, and I still can't carry a note. She was my inhale to her exhale. We awoke every day holding each other even though we would go to bed clinging to the opposite sides of the bed to get the best light for reading from our nightstands. Hell, she taught me how to live. And now she is teaching me how to die with class and dignity. That is so her.

We didn't have children, couldn't. It was me. But boy, did we have fun trying. For years I told her we could adopt. We even looked into it, but a vacation or big event would roll around and she would say "Let's look at it in the fall" or beyond the next party or holiday. I often thought she didn't press the idea so I wouldn't feel inadequate. I think if there was a blessing to not having children I am living it now.

I think, no…I know that it would have destroyed her understanding she was going to leave our children without a mother. Some say having kids might have prolonged her fight, but I can't even imagine the suffering she would be going through knowing she wasn't going to be there to take care of the kids like she took care of me.

2

The most gut wrenching?
I wake up standing over her side of the empty bed sobbing.
Could this get anymore fucked?

When you are watching someone you love die your brain
turns to mush. You have thoughts that no sane person would
have. Driving to the hospital one morning knowing that her
parents are coming into town for a visit, I find myself wishing
they were dead. Now I have nothing against them, but every time
they come, my wife feels like she has let them down, and I react
poorly to that. It takes a day or so of reassuring from me that she
didn't. Oddly, they aren't as reassuring. I swear her dad blames me
for all of this shit. I guess it is his way of dealing with the pain.
Her folks are old, but I am sure they envisioned stepping around
me at picnics to pick up their grandchildren and kiss their
daughter at this stage of their lives. Instead they are visiting a
hospital, stepping around me to watch their dying daughter
apologize about her hair missing, or the fact that the hospital
room is too warm or too cold, whatever they want to bitch about
this time.

They ask me questions when she dozes, hoping for a
small bit of good news – but there is none to share, so we ease
into polite conversation. Gardening tips or sports scores. Wait,

here's a good one, when my wife asks them how they are doing, they spend no fewer than ten minutes whining about their health issues. Can't keep food down, his back hurts, her arthritis is really acting up. I find humor in this: parents complaining about health issues to their dying daughter. So what does she do? She listens and makes some recommendations. Then she wants to get their doctor on the phone so she can grill him like she used to.

I know they blame me for all of this. No grandkids, and now I killed their daughter. We didn't live under a high voltage line. We ate healthfully, drank bottled water, and exercised every day. But I can tell he blames me. Did I ever mention to them that Mom had two bouts of breast cancer and Dad has prostate cancer? What do you think she was going to die of with that family tree, old age? Blame me for killing her? No parent should ever have to bury a child. Like I said, you think and say things an insane person would only say when you are watching someone you love die. Your mind turns simply to mush.

I remember watching movies where the heroine loses her beloved. She is given the news and just collapses. For years, I thought how corny it was for a person to faint or to become hysterical or such an emotional mess that they require a sedative or a doctor's care. Movie lines like, "I don't think I should be alone," or "I gave her a sedative" seemed so Hollywood. But as our final act plays out and I am one of the leads, I don't think anyone who just lost someone or, like me, is in the process of losing someone through the slow erosion of cancer, should be left alone. We shouldn't be allowed to drive or make the simplest of decisions. As I have learned: You are not all there. I wish someone would give me a sedative.

Since the inevitable became real to me and we fell from hopeful to hospice, I have found these hypnotized episodes occurring more frequently. I will sit in the hospital cafeteria and can't remember what I did an hour ago, not a clue. I am losing chunks of my entire day.

Over the last few months I would be startled out of these hypnotic jags. I am not asleep. It is as if someone says,

8

"When I count to three, I will snap my fingers and you will awake." The finger snap is usually a horn blast or siren. The noise would snap me back to reality. I would find myself jolted out of one of these episodes to find myself driving my car on a busy street! I don't know where I am going, who I was going to visit, or what errand I was running. Instead of trying to remember, I just point the car toward the hospital. I have drifted in these pain commas at red lights, in the middle of conversations, at work and anytime I have a moment to feel sorry for myself. Three times I have awoken in the bathtub in the middle of the night. I haven't taken a bath since I was a child. I have found myself standing on our front porch in my underwear at dawn, as if I am watching and awaiting an arrival. Pathetic. The most gut wrenching? I wake up standing over her side of the empty bed, sobbing. Could this get any more fucked?

These hypnotic episodes begin by something triggering a memory of a good time. I was rummaging through a drawer looking for a working pen. I need to fill out more insurance forms. I find two red, plastic cocktail drink straws. They are from drinks we had had on an airplane a while back. We had taken a weekend getaway flight to Chicago. As we were drinking and passing the time, she took my drink straw and hers and braided them together like you would a child's hair. With every twist of the straw we had to tell each other what we loved most about each other. Needless to say we ran out of straw before we ran out of what to say. She put the straw in her purse and told me she would keep it just in case I forgot why I loved her so much. She told me she would keep it forever in a safe place. I guess forever ends next week if you believe doctors.

Just as the memory brings a slight smile to my face, as I set aside for a moment the vomiting and clumps of hair in my hand, the scene abruptly changes from a dream to a nightmare. I flash to a razor sharp, Technicolor memory of our doctor saying the word "cancer" and that look in her eyes. God! That look in her beautiful eyes. In the past, I always could help her, protect her, and if I had to, save her. I can't do any of that. Not with this. She is alone. Sure I am with her, near her, but she is alone and that look; it will never stop haunting me.

9

As the nightmare continues, I become physically ill. I go from mad to hate, to self-pity, and then I switch on the numbness and bam, I'm gone. I thought this was an involuntary reaction to all the pain, but as I begin another month of driving back and forth from home to hospital to work to hospital to home, I have determined that I have created the comas, these episodes, in my attempt to survive. I can switch them on and off now at my leisure.

I was at the end of one of these hypnotic episodes when I was interrupted by the blasts of a car horn behind me. When I finally got my bearings, the guy had gone around me and I was still idling at the intersection waiting for the light to cycle back to green. I wondered how many green lights I sat through. I actually chuckled when thinking of the Beatles' lyrics "He blew his mind out in a car. He didn't notice that the light had changed." I wonder if John Lennon, who wrote that, had a wife who was about to die.

Just as the light turned green I saw the oddest thing. In a strip mall, next to a coffee shop, in an abandoned storefront was a man of no particular consequence standing in the window of the empty store, holding a white placard. It's the cheap cardboard you get at the drugstore with the school supplies, the kind that your folks would buy so you can do your 4th grade current events project. The same crappy thin placard you can see someone at a sporting event holding up saying, I HEART 17 or some shit. I was focused on not causing another traffic scene, so I pressed hard on the accelerator and shot through the intersection. My speed and lack of interest did not afford me a look at his sign. I figured he was just another nut bag looking for some attention or hustling money. Asshole.

When someone you really love is slowly dying you become an expert in things you wish you never had to – like cancer. Does anyone really want to hear about the mother fucker called cancer? Never! Knowing what I know now and seeing what I have seen, I wouldn't tell a soul just so I could spare them the pain of knowing. I wish a bus had hit my wife or that she was in a plane crash: quick, simple, and final. Cancer kills you by the pound. Ounce by ounce, the life, the color, the joy are slowly sucked out of your being like a tire with a slow leak. There are no blow-outs with cancer. Cancer is calculating and patient.

Have you ever seen workers move a house to another location or transport a rocket to the launch pad on one of those, huge, caterpillar flatbeds? It inches along at something like 50 feet every 2 hours. Cancer is slower. It starts with the good things first. Kiss the good days goodbye. From the moment you are told you have cancer, the good days all disappear. Even if you have a good day it is only because you were both drunk and left your memories and common sense at the bottom of a tequila bottle. In the morning, cancer waits for you to awaken with your hangover. It doesn't care. It just makes it hurt more. What really sucks in the early stages was that she was fit as a fiddle. You wouldn't have known she was ill.

Forget about sharing a newspaper or watching television together. Every show has someone dying in it. Every news report is telling you that so-and-so passed away. Then both of you play the "Age & Disease" game. It's a simple enough game: When you read or hear that someone has died, you immediately compare their age and what killed them to your situation or in my case, my wife's cancer. Then you finish the game by spending the next 20 minutes talking yourself into the idea that that is not happening to you both of you. Us.

The emotional pain doesn't need physical reminders to destroy you. It is so powerful it never lets a waking moment pass without nudging at your psyche. Every time we catch each other's glance I see the pain in her eyes, the fear of the unknown, the fear of death, and my inability to fix it. Yeah . . . Cancer kills you by the pound ounce by ounce. By the time cancer erodes you physically your mind is already composted gray mulch.

When you are around someone you love who is about to die, they slip through your fingers like a fistful of sand: granule by granule. No movie endings here. Cancer takes its time at the end as well. She sleeps now most of the day. Her breathing has become irregular, and when food is brought to her she cannot stay awake long enough to eat it.

I sleep with her now. I don't care what they say. What is
left of her body I hold in my arms. It is just me crying now. God!
The pain is immeasurable. She woke at three o'clock in the
afternoon and was shivering. Have you ever felt or tried to stay
warm with a hospital blanket? It has the weight and the warmth of
a paper napkin. There is just no love in those blankets. I asked her
softly if she would like the quilt from our bed at home. She
smiled. No speaking, she was too weak, just a smile. There was no
one here to send over to our house to fetch it. I asked the doctor
if I would miss anything if I left for 20 minutes to get her quilt.
He knew what I was asking. He checked her vitals and said no,
but to hurry just in case.

I sped home and tore the quilt from our bed. I have to
stop for a moment and wrap my face in it to smell her healthy, to
smell us just one more time. I knew as soon as I delivered this
quilt to her it would have the smell of death on it, and I wanted to
savor her one last time like she was when she was alive.
I folded the quilt with care, just like she would like: corners tucked
square, equal layering just so. My mind leapt to a vision of marines
in dress blues at a military funeral, meticulously cross folding the
quilt and presenting it to me as I sit next to her coffin. Snap out of
it! Focus! No time for an episode. Gingerly, I set the quilt on the
car seat next to me and am off.

Speeding, rolling stop signs, running yellow/red lights, I
took a short cut one of the nurses had told me about to avoid
rush hour traffic. My mom used to call the red lights she went
through, when they were changing from yellow to red: pink. I
could use my mom's sense of humor right about now.

I was a few blocks from the hospital and was thinking I
had to thank the nurse for that short cut information when I got
stuck at a red light, a long red light with left turn arrows and a
school crossing. Shit! Now I am fully committed to getting my
wife our quilt before she leaves me, I wanted to race through the
red light but a police cruiser was also waiting for the light to
change. Nervously, I craned my neck to look for an escape: a back
alley or something, anything!

As I scan to the left I saw "that guy," the one I saw last week, with the cardboard sign, standing in another empty storefront window. Was this the same guy I had noticed a few days before? Hell, I can't tell if this guy is a hallucination from one of my past episodes or if he's actually standing there in the window of this empty store. What are the chances? Forget about him! Focus on the quilt and this damn red light. "Change, damn it!"

I can't. Maybe I am punchy or have totally gone mad, but I am drawn back to this guy. Was he the same guy or not? I couldn't shake the idea of the same guy: here, now and looking at me. Strange, what was he doing there? Now he is here, miles from the first place standing in another empty store. My brain is putty. It can't be the same guy. Stop it! Forget it!

I am not good with names, but I do remember faces. I have had horrid nightmares but have never imagined or conjured a person and dropped them into real life while I was this awake, this coherent. Shit! That *is* the same guy?! Dressed the same with jeans, flannel shirt, but the thing that was really unique and why I am pretty sure it was the same guy was he had an army boot on one foot and what looked like a gym shoe on the other. He wore a green Army jacket, had dirty hands and an unshaven face, and his hair was a long, scraggly mess. Yep, that was him! He had to be homeless for sure.

Not now! Let it go! Twisting in my sweaty car seat, again I look around for an escape. She needs this quilt and she needs it now. But that fucking light stayed locked on red. People waiting with me began to beep their horns, chiding the people in the front of the lanes to roll through it. Shit! If this light doesn't change, cop or no cop, I am going on the sidewalk!

I again glance to my left, and now the homeless guy is staring at me, is motioning to me with his right hand to get my attention. But to do what? He points to the sign in his left hand. He wants me to read his stupid sign. Pick on someone with a healthy wife. He becomes more animated and starts to motion to his sign with much more fervor. Who gives a shit especially now, I

13

can't read it - who cares what it says? WILL WORK FOR
FOOD? HOMELESS, NEED A JOB? What the fuck do I care
what you want!

I am about ready to put down my window and tell him
to fuck off, but in a flash the light turns green, and I am off. As I
rifled past the store where he is standing, I want to look to see if
he starts picking on someone else -as homeless people typically do
after they decide you are blowing them off. I take one more
curious glance to see if he has lost interest in me. Instead his stare
is riveted to me and my fleeting car. The sign he was holding
casually in his left hand, he is now holding with both hands, high
above his head, making it easier for me to see it while moving
away from him: TALK TO GOD. What? "Talk to God"? The
fucking sign, today, this guy wanted me to see says "Talk to
God?" Is my luck and timing that bad? Could it have said
anything worse? Today? Screw God! He is in the process of taking
the only woman I really love away from me - if you believe in that
crap.

I thought I believed in God up until about six months
ago, but no real God lets that kind of prolonged pain take a
person like my wife. She is loving, meek, and would never hurt a
living thing. Everyone who meets her loves her, thinks she is
funny, thoughtful, and caring. She treats strangers with the same
care as she does family. If there is a God, my wife would be the
poster child for how God-fearing people should act and look.
There is no God. God and religion are nothing more than a
fucking illusion to give people something to do on Sundays before
they watch football or beat their dogs and children.

"Talk to God!" "Talk to God?"

My curiosity has turned to rage. I roll down my window,
and catching the guys glance, I flip him off. I have a quilt to
deliver! Sorry, don't have time to talk to God! I have to go watch
my only true love die, someone who can't talk anymore, and
someone who prayed for Your help and got dick!

Where was "God" when I needed him? Where were the fucking miracles? What did you do with all those fucking prayers I said? Weren't you listening then? Didn't you want to talk back then? Did you need more money in the donation basket? Were you too busy watching professional athletes praying to you? You talk to God you mother fucker, I have to hold my wife while she dies, fucking asshole.

I don't know who that homeless guy was and he didn't deserve that. But it sure felt good.

3

*You really can't tell the dead weight of someone you love
until they die in your arms.*

I park my car in the emergency room parking lot of the hospital. I have learned if you want to park close with the shortest walk to the ICU, that's the place to get in fast. Going to a hospital every-day for six months affords you some perks. Security guards, hospital staff, and volunteers get to know you and know why you are there. My car used to get ticketed and towed in the first month, but no longer. They know me, and they know my car.

When I bolt past the admissions desk in the emergency room, quilt in hand, no one says a word. They hear the pace of my footsteps on the linoleum floor. This is not a "normal" cancer victim day: We are about to die. They know it. They are aware I am not going to be coming out the same person I came in as. They've seen that fucked look on faces before. They know I am about to become half a person. These are the perks of spending the last six months of your marriage in a hospital watching someone you love die.

I get to the room, and to my surprise she seems more coherent than she has been in a week or so. When she sees the quilt she smiles. She raises her left hand maybe an inch or two up from her side. This has become her way to beckon me or respond to someone, to let me or someone visiting know she appreciates their time. In its simplest form the gesture alerts me that she is

16

still alive. Her left hand raises and a slight smile is all that cancer allows her to muster. Want a simple pleasure? When I see that left hand move I know she isn't gone yet, and I relax a little bit. She is fighting, gliding on morphine, just holding on for one more Sunday morning breakfast, one more walk together, one more sunny day on the beach. Fuck it hurts!

Honeymooning in Cancun, I remember thinking how wonderful her engagement ring and wedding band looked on her tanned left hand while we lay on the beach. I worked an extra job for 6 months to pay for that ring and the trip. It didn't have a huge stone, kind of in the middle, but it was a perfect size for her long, slender and very sexy hand. She loved the rings. I loved the fact that she loved them.

I remember thinking that I had no business having this woman love me. She moved naturally with style and ease. When we walked along the beach or lounged around the pool, I watched guys stealing glances at her. By now I was used to it, but it sure made me feel good. I tried to hold in my gut and throw back my shoulders so I didn't look like this pathetic, dumpy older brother, mooching a vacation from my successful sister, or a stumpy rich guy with a trophy wife. It became my goal - my duty - to earn and keep this woman every day. If I would have ever told her that that's the way I felt, she would have thought I was an idiot. She just didn't care about any of that - at least she never told me she cared.

Her skin always looked tanned, naturally golden brown. She had that Italian olive skin with Caribbean, blue-water eyes and golden hair, a model's figure with perky curves in all in the right places, and a double-take, girl-next-door face. I used to joke with our friends that I thought she was blind or just felt sorry for me. There wasn't a guy who met us who didn't take the time to stare at her and then tell me what a lucky guy I was.

I figured she would eventually wise up and dump me, especially since I was the reason we couldn't have children, but she never did. Besides her outward beauty she had a heart of gold. And she was mine.

17

Her left hand is now affixed to a board. Bloodied and bruised from needles searching for veins, veins with cancer coursing through them. Her hand has withered. If I didn't know it was hers, I would think it was not human or it came from an exhumed mummy. They took her rings awhile back with all her other personal effects and jewelry. The person processing her into the "going to die" ward of the hospital, the place where the only drug administered is morphine, handed them all to me in a plastic bag with her last name and patient number on it. He then looked at me and said with a chilly ease, "Make sure you remember where you put these because you will want them for the funeral home." Seriously, did I need that? Did I look that fucking whacked out of my brain to need that icy comment?

A week ago I brought the rings back to her. She wanted them. I placed them on her left hand, ring finger as I did the night I asked her to marry me. It was the last tear she ever cried. I asked her again that day in the hospital, "Would you marry me"? She smiled, raised her left hand, and I slid the rings back in place, in the right place. The rings were twice the size now for what remained of her ring finger. Boney and pale, yellow, dried flesh with finger - nails the exact same, fucked yellow color. No more, warm, golden brown, olive exterior. No more boys staring at her. Only her boy; me.

Another thing they don't tell you when someone you love is dying of cancer is that the shit that they pump into you to prolong death turns your skin, your eyeballs and your fingernails all piss-in-a-cup yellow. I didn't care. The rings looked beautiful on her. I found some hospital tape and taped them onto her finger. Then, I read our wedding vows, both her part and mine. When done, I tell her a story, a happy thought, we haven't had many, of her being cured and going home, healthy, to take to heaven with her. Fuck this hurts. "We are on our way back to home now", I whispered to her.

I used painstaking details to describe the trip home. I began with her being cured, wheeling out of the hospital with applause from the doctors. I whisper the details of the drive to the house on the sunniest of days, the lawn neatly manicured, and the house in pristine order like she left it. I know this sounds stupid but I want her last memory to be her fondest memory. The doctors say that she probably can't hear me now, but I don't care.

I crawl into bed with her. I enfold her in my arms. She seems so frail, so small. I tuck up the quilt around our chins. I hold her head in the crook of my arm and kiss her softly over and over and over and over and over again. I dare not squeeze her too tightly or she will moan in pain. She feels the size and strength of a small child. I hum our favorite song to her, "Always and Forever," by a group called Heat Wave. If you have ever been to a wedding you have heard it. She drifts in and out of consciousness.

Exhausted, I too doze in and out. Around 2:00 A.M. her breathing becomes different, more irregular than ever. I immediately become keenly aware of everything about her. My senses are never sharper: shallow breathing, she becomes more listless if that is possible. I whisper "I love you!" I dare not say, "don't leave me!" I don't want her to feel guilty like she always does if she thinks she has disappointed me. I just keep whispering "I love you." I put my left hand, wedding ring fingered and all on her chest and feel the heartbeats start to drip further and further apart.

I hold her close. And in that instant I feel and hear the last breath escape her body. No more inhales. No more weak heartbeats. Where will I put my hand now? Who will I hold? Who will I talk to? No more gasping for breath after we finish jogging. No more heavy breathing before and after we make love. No big gulps of air during a belly laugh.

Her body slumps in my arms, lifeless. I wail; "NO!" Insane, I try to wake her, try to coax one last smile, one last twinkle from her blue, blue eyes. But alas, I can feel her entire weight of her body slumped in my arms. You really can't tell the dead weight of someone you love until they die in your arms.

She is gone.

4

*Nobody ever tells you that when you give yourself
to someone you love deeply and they die,
they take your love with them.*

The alarms of the life's support monitors following her decline were shut off in our room days ago. The staff is watching from the cheap seats at the nurse's station. They don't rush in when she goes. They know I am there with her. And they don't come in for a full ten minutes. My head swirls, I can't feel my own being. When I move I feel as if I am under water. I can't breathe. I can't move from this spot. I don't want to move. I want to lay there with her. I want to go with her. I want to kill myself. I miss her.

"You promised you would never leave me! YOU PROMISED!"

After a minute that seems like an hour, something hits me like a cold bucket of water, thrown in the face: I am transfixed, not on the pain or loss, but on what she would want me to do NOW. I flip on the lights in the room. I look at her lifeless body. I focus. I adjust the bed upright into the sitting position. I straighten the covers and quilt like she wanted it when she was expecting visitors. I place her hands by her side, gently pull all those fucking tubes out of her, and make sure her rings are on for a little while longer. What few strands of her hair remain, I move back off her face and adjust her head to be square with her shoulders, the way she carried herself when she walked. I make sure her pajamas from home are pulled down to their proper length, no longer bunched up around her thighs, and that she has socks on her feet.

My attention turns to the room. I move the tray table back into its stored position and toss away any loose newspapers and magazines. I put the uncomfortable chair back in its corner for the next victim's spouse and throw away any wilted flowers and old cards.

When the room is to "our" liking, presentable for guests, I lean over and kiss her one last time on the lips, cold and turning gray, I don't care. I whisper.

"I will always love you."

I then sit on the edge of the bed, hold her hand, and ring for the nurse. I find myself not in any hurry. We just sit there together like we did in so many places before: vacations, the back deck, even at the stupid landfill, waiting in line to recycle cans. It didn't matter where we were. All that mattered is that "we were" and were together. We didn't require any plucky banter or interesting anecdotes, no topical discussion of current events, just comfortable, totally-in-love-and-we-both-know-it silence.

Just as I find myself feeling a little unattended to, our night nurse peers around the corner of the door. We have become close friends over the past few months. When my wife still had the energy to speak, she called her alma mater to put in a good word for the nurse's oldest son who was trying to get into the state university. She was so impressed with my wife's level of giving, even in the worst of times. When he received his letter of acceptance she couldn't stop thanking her. We really didn't know if her recommendation did anything to affect his acceptance into the school, but the nurse had never had a total stranger help her or her family before - especially a terminally ill cancer victim. She just never had a chance to meet my wife before the sick times. Like anyone else she would have loved her. From that moment on, the special creature comforts that are afforded politicians, dignitaries, or rich people were all delivered to my wife - including a private room.

The nurse is a large African American woman, hair straightened, neat, with her generous size always putting a strain on whatever scrubs she is wearing, material pulled tightly around her back side and thighs, and her bosoms always bursting out the V-neck shirt. She must weigh no less than three hundred pounds, laughs like a truck driver, and speaks like one as well if anyone gives her any grief. She makes a whisking noise when she walks, her thighs always rubbing together. I couldn't help envy her larger than life appearance at that moment compared to my wife's lifeless remains. It is so stark, the comparison between a healthy, happy, soul and what remains after a six month cancer carpet bombing. I look at my wife and think: We have traveled so far down such a bad road, baby rest now, the journey is over.

The night nurse doesn't say a word, but offers a half smile, mouth closed, sympathetic. She has tears in her eyes. I think I am okay, but when I say…

"She's gone."

…and I see the tears while she nods her head to say yes, she knows, my throat tightens and swells. I cannot speak. She shakes her head with a mom's "it's going to be okay" look. She walks slowly toward me, not wanting to misread my emotional state. She doesn't. I need someone to lean on. And she just holds me. I wrap my right arm around her as she bear hugs me. I tighten my grip on my wife's left hand, wishing she was there to feel my love just one more time.

I sit with her until the doctor comes to pronounce her dead. Then they take her away from me. And for the first time it occurs to me that after 18 years I am now all alone. I don't know what to do. I don't know where to go. Nobody ever tells you that when you give yourself to someone you love deeply and they die, they take your love with them. I have now been hallowed. I am half the man I was an hour ago.

Without my rudder I have been set adrift. I walk down the hall of the hospital looking for a quiet place to call her parents, family, and friends. I need to vomit. My head is swirling, my knees are beaten-boxer wobbly. My mouth is dry. How can I make these phone calls? How can I face everyone? She was the one they loved. She was everyone's best friend. She was the babe all the guys wanted. She was the life of the party. I was the one who got the coats, ruined the photographs and carried the luggage. I was the guy everyone was surprised she married. Now I remain. And everybody will wonder why I am breathing, and she is gone.

I remember the private, family conference room on floor six, the cancer ward, the room where our doctor ushered me in one day to tell me that the chemotherapy was not slowing the cancer and I should prepare for the worst. This is the most fucked room in the hospital. You may think the morgue. Nope, those people are dead; they feel no pain and their families' know there is no coming back. But in these little cancer conference rooms, these crematoria of optimism, this is where the crushing news is delivered with a sledgehammer. This is where you learn to cry so hard your belly cramps. This is where they plunger your heart and soul into a meat grinder and you watch it spill out, in slow motion onto the table. This is the room we were sentenced to death by a judge masquerading as a doctor. And there lies the true pain: You get a death sentence even though you committed no crime. You mumble the word "why" quite a bit afterward.

I wonder how many people actually ever return to this room to tell family the same news they have received months earlier. Odd, ironic, and I think fitting. Why fuck up another place on the planet with horrible memories for the rest of my life? I might as well keep my personal Auschwitz in the same room of pain. Your mind plays games with you when you have just lost the only person in life you truly loved.

My turn on the rack was no different six months ago. Our doctor placed his hand on my shoulder, said he was sorry, and walked out, leaving me in an eight-by-ten-foot room with a small table, two chairs, a box of Kleenex, and the chore of telling my wife she is about to die. I stare at a pastel painting of two

23

kittens frolicking with a ball of yarn hanging on the wall. I think to myself, "She fucking hates cats."

There is a numbing that occurs when you have to call family and friends and tell them their best friend; favorite niece, closest sister, or daughter has died. Popular, loving, caring people have more friends than jerks like me; I don't know how many more times I can cry. The first call is to her parents. I wonder if I should wait until six. He answers the phone on the first ring. He knows it was me. I say hello and his first response is, "Do you know what time it is?" I just press on and say, "She's gone." He asks when. I tell him the time. He says they will be there by lunchtime and then hangs up the phone. Icy. I am sure they have their own pain to bathe in.

I find myself having trouble dialing her phone. Wet hands and a small keyboard make for frustrating times in the cancer conference room. She gave it to me when she was planning this moment, even programmed and charged the phone. She didn't want anyone she wanted to know about her death missed. Exhausted, emotions frayed, I press on. The same words are coming out of my mouth over and over again but it sounded like "blah, blah, blah" to me.

I start calling a few names I am unfamiliar with off the bottom of the list instead of working from top to bottom like I was instructed to. This way I can practice on distant friends until I get better at this before I get to brothers, sisters, and close friends. I find myself becoming less and less anguished, the process becoming task-focused because I want to finish as fast as I can. When I sense I have it right, I call her brothers and sisters.

I can't even get out one word before the screams of pain echo through the receiver: phones hitting the floor, hysterical crying and me, consoling them. Yeah me, the town crier, consoling them. I am surrounded by death, pain, and loneliness, and when I call her brothers and sisters the volume of the pain is deafening.

I call her favorite uncle next. I wish I had called him first. He reacts like I think my dad probably would have in these circumstances if he was still with me. Her uncle is kind, loving, and extremely sympathetic. He is also very upbeat and strong. He tells me to "hang in there," and to "keep my chin up," "she would have wanted you that way." He asks me if there is anyone there with me. I tell him no. He is puzzled by the lack of family. Then he pauses, letting me off the hook to ask if he and his wife can help by calling remaining friends and family. I give him a few names and numbers to help out with, people so distant that I don't even know them. I am sure they are people at work or old college friends. I think though that it should be me calling the list because she told me to.

I finish my last call three hours after I began, just as the phone is running out of juice. I get to leave the cancer conference room. I was done disseminating pain for the morning.

5

TALK TO GOD! TALK TO GOD?
You talk to God you asshole! I have no God!
God is a prick! God took my wife.
Tell Him when you talk to Him next, I want my wife back!

When I leave the hospital this morning there is a brilliant blue sky and sunny day. What a fuckin' waste of good weather. I find my car parked in two spots, crooked. I was running in with the quilt when I parked it, and am surprised I navigated it in even that well. I buckle myself in and feel the warm air rising off the sun-saturated dashboard and seats. The windows have been up all morning and it is cooking in here. The warmth feels good. I leave the windows up. I start the car, put my hands on the wheel to back out and leave when it dawns on me: I have nowhere to go. Go home? Home is where the heart is, and mine is dead, left back in the hospital. I can't go home right now, I have no children to console, no pets to feed, couldn't go to work. I am a mess. Everything that is my life just died. I have filled my entire life with her, and now my entire life is empty.

Now what? What to do? Where to go? I look over at the passenger seat. The plastic bag of her personal effects is all that survived the cancer. Oh, shit! I need to go to the funeral home! She had it all picked out, even storing the number on my cell phone. I call and tell them I am on my way over. I have a

26

destination! As stupid as that sounds, I feel relief, I don't have to stay in the parking lot in my car wondering what to do. She always knew.

I back the car out from the spot and lumber toward the exit. I get to the attendant's booth – yet another pal you get to meet when you spend six months parking in the same lot. I look at him: he knows or at least he seems to know, nods and waves me through without speaking or having me pay. The day your wife dies parking is free. I am just bitter. I return the nod and fashion a slight smile, mumble thanks through the closed window. Will this fucking ever get better?

I leave the parking lot with a pretty good idea of where the funeral home is. We passed it a number of times. It was by her office. We found it one day when she was admiring the old, southern, plantation style architecture of this very large house. She loved the wrap-around porch. When we slowed to take a closer look, we saw the unobtrusive funeral home ground sign. We thought at first that it was a historical marker. She said, "That's the kind of funeral home I like," meaning one that didn't look like a funeral home, meaning she had no interest in anything to do with funeral homes for at least for another 40 or so years - and now I am on my way to that very place. I remember thinking I liked it because it didn't have any of that cheesy, fake, green Astroturf, glued to any of the ramps or sidewalks in the portico or entrances - that same shit they lump over the pile of dirt at a cemetery for a burial. I hope now they don't have that at her funeral. Her funeral. Oh my fucking God!

I am driving the speed limit, and for me that is slow. I am always a five over the speed limit kind of guy. I am in no hurry today, I have no interest in reaching my destination. I'm looking out the window for anything to take my mind off my loneliness while squinting for address numbers. I know I am close but my mind just isn't functioning. The simple stuff seems hard. I start getting hot with the windows up. I go from feeling cozy to sweaty and put the windows down to let some fresh air into the car. I smell freshly cut grass, a personal favorite of mine. I slow a bit to prolong the aroma. My mind drifts off to bygone days when I was a child mowing lawns – those simpler times before love and the pain of losing it. But I am startled out of my daydream.

I see that guy from the storefront windows walking a few hundred yards ahead of me on my side of the street. Fuck!

"This can't be the same guy?"

I mumble to myself. My eyes are playing tricks on me. Next thing I'll see is my wife with Big Foot. Nope, it can't be. We are a half hour's drive from where I saw him last. It would take him an entire day to walk here. Impossible, it can't be the same guy. It does look like him, though. Nah. No way.

Well, maybe? Should I stop to apologize for flipping him off? Did he even see me flipping him off? I don't even know if this is really the same guy. It looks like him. Screw it. I am a mess. I am sure he doesn't remember me even if that is him; he looks like a meth head. He couldn't tell the difference between me and a garbage can. He probably waves his stupid sign at hundreds of people a day. He won't remember me. Thoughts, memories and pain have been so mashed together for the last few months, I can't say for sure if he was the guy I saw before or even if what I saw was real. I'll just drive right past. I gun the engine and lock my focus forward, just wanting to pass by my mirage - no conflict, no sign, no problem.

I've got to look! I have to see if this is "my guy." I have to make sure I am not going crazy. I squeeze a quick glance out of the corner of my right eye. Shit! That is him! That is the guy in the window with the sign! I draw even with him, without looking up or even altering his gait he holds up that fucking sign: TALK TO GOD. Drive! Drive! Drive! Is this chump following me? Shit! Shit! Shit! In my rearview mirror, he is holding the sign over his head now, directing it at me! TALK TO GOD TALK TO GOD! You talk to God you asshole! I have no God! God is a prick! God took my wife. Tell Him when you talk to Him next, I want my wife back!

I am trembling. If there is anything left of me emotionally I just left it back there with Mr. Sign. You become physically and emotionally exhausted when your wife has just died and someone decides to fuck with you!

I make it to the funeral home and was there too early. The woman who greets me tells me the funeral director is still collecting my wife and I should go home and get a photo of her and that the clothes were delivered a month ago. So her. I just sit in my car, shirt wet through with sweat, fumbling with my wife's personal items in that plastic hospital sandwich bag. I think I am losing my mind. My wife dies. This nut shows up. He is real; isn't he? I don't want to go home. It will hurt too much. Fuck!

I sit in the middle of the living room floor with eight shoe boxes of photos. She liked stills. Our memories, were in perfect order. Every moment of our relationship she has photographed, developed, and put in chronological order in these shoe boxes. Each shoe box must have 500 photos in it, front to back. Each box has a start date when the first photo in the box was taken and the date for the last photo in the box. The dates she printed on the short side of the boxes remind me of a gravestone marker with the born and died dates. Shots of everything we did together are captured for history in four by six glossy prints.

The first box probably flies the farthest. It catches the dining room chandelier, hits the edge of the doorway leading to the kitchen, and splatters across the slippery ceramic tile floor. Those glossy photos slide effortlessly across her clean, waxed floor. She would buff it every Saturday morning. Walk in there too soon on a Saturday and your ass was grass.

Those photos slide from one end of the kitchen to the other. My mind is black hate. My mental muscle memory stops me for a moment. Oh shit! She is going to be pissed when she sees what I did to the photos and her kitchen. Then the evil comes with a vengeance. She isn't coming home this time! She isn't coming back to scold me or clean up my mess! She is dead! She is fucking dead! She is gone, and she is never coming back!

29

She is dead! She is fucking dead! Cancer killed her, and now it's killing me!

There is strong urge to lie down on the floor in a fetal ball when you are drowning in a sea of four by six glossy photos of the dead woman you love so much.

I lay there for what seems hours. It has gotten dark, and I can hear sounds of the neighborhood settling: fewer cars going by, no screaming kids, distant barking, and summer crickets. I fall asleep between the refrigerator and back door. When I awake I lift myself off the floor, one of the photos sticks to my cheek. My tears, sweat, and the shiny substance that makes photos glossy have fused the photo to my face. I slowly peel it off and am about to toss back into the pile when I see her smiling, glowing face in the photo. She always took great photos, but this photo was taken when she was at her best: radiant and confident. A slight smile crosses my lips. I mumble...

"I love you."

...stick the photo in my shirt pocket, and head back to the funeral home.

There's a numbing that occurs when words that you never expect to say come out of your mouth. I never was a person who struggled with nightmares but I know this must be what night terror is like - but I never wake up. When do I get to wake up?

The funeral director is showing me back into the bowels of the creepiest building I have ever been in. And she is here too? Shit! I want to go. Small talk. Small talk. Focus!

I tell the funeral director she made plans to donate her body to her university's medical department. We had made fun of it when she had come home with the donor applications a few years ago. We joked, saying, "Who would ever want our wrinkled old bodies? And we were right. Donating your body to science is different than donating your eyes or other organs. There is more of a formal application requiring witnesses, and even though you sign up, if loved ones don't want you to donate your body, they can still back out. I would never think of not fulfilling her wishes.

When the representatives from the College of Medicine come to the hospital morgue to take her back to the university where we met, where we fell in love, where she graduated with honors, they deny her acceptance, this time to the freshman class of dead cadavers. Her body has been emaciated to the point of looking sub-human. She fought the devil two months longer than anyone expected. The doctor says; "Three months to live" and she fights for five. But what no one ever tells you about cancer is the longer you fight to stay alive, the more time the cancer has to eat your body from the inside out. The university is not surprised to find her body a hollowed carcass. They know her. They knew she was a stubborn scrapper. There was no quit in her, but they pass and decline the donation.

It would have been so much simpler. University takes the body. I rent a room. We have a memorial service. I get drunk - then shoot myself in the fucking head. Nope, too easy; we have to do this the hard way.

We enter a room that is a mix between a butcher shop and a scene from Saw One or was it Saw Two? Fuck, I don't remember. But the room looked fucking creepy. He wants me to see what progress he has made already before they are to lay her out in one of those just-as-creepy, viewing rooms. He did not wait for the photo. The room smells like antiseptic death. He walks comfortably around the stainless steel gurneys with a drain for blood. Saws and shit that I can't explain their function, are on a tray next to the gurney. It is a torture chamber for people that no longer feel. The funeral director was nicer in the sales part of our relationship, but now he is fucking Jeffrey Dommer incarnate. Shit! My fucking skin is crawling. I really don't want to see her, see her here, see her dead. That cold, lifeless, I'm-in-a-funeral-home, I know she is fucking dead; dead.

I think I might have been shown into the wrong room. I hardly recognize her. In fact it is not her. I am sure the funeral director has made every - attempt to capture her living image, but the person on this cruel table is not my wife. This dead woman has on my wife's dress, but it is three sizes too big. She looks like she inherited it from a fat older sister.

You can see where they have cut out the back of the garment and folded it under to try to make it fit. The wig looks like it was bought on the cheap: shiny, Barbie, plastic hair. Where the fuck did that come from? It looks like it was placed on backward and fashioned in a hairstyle my wife would never wear. It would look better as part of a Halloween costume.

You don't see many women like my wife. She was one of those types who could try on any article of clothing, and it instantly looked like it was made for her. She never fussed much with her hair. Washed it, pulled it back, or wore it down, but it always looked like she worked on it for days. You want sexy? With a quick grab, a gathering pull, and a twist she would put up her hair and stab it with what looked like a knitting needle. We'd sit on the porch in the summer evenings and when the sun was ready to halve itself behind the hill, those fat, yellow-orange, lingering few rays would cast a brilliant spotlight on her neck. Wisps of blond, baby hair danced in the breeze. I would have to focus hard and control myself so as to not to take her right then and there when we had people over. She was an angel.

I start to explain to the funeral director that she never wears her hair like that. He gives me an "I tried" look, and before he can offer an excuse, I dismiss his explanation with a kind smile and slight wave of my hand.

I decide the casket is to be closed when I see the woman's face on this body spackled with brown stucco theater makeup. Caked, meat wrapping paper beige and has been slathered over her emaciated, skeletal face. Lipstick or perhaps paint, has been used to describe her lip line. It is the same color as the dress: wine. She never wore lipstick, didn't have to, and she would have never thought of wearing a deep wine colored lip anything. I don't know how they did it, but that lipstick made her look deader.

The dress's neck line sags below where it is supposed to be supported by her chest. You notice exactly where the stucco job stops and the actual gray-blue pocked skin begins just above her chemo port. I quickly try tucking the neck line up to cover it but it was so loose, her once strong shoulders could no longer carry the weight of the dress.

Her hands are crossed at the waist. Again the shit brown skin paint all over her arms and hands, nails painted that shit wine color, and her rings - an engagement and wedding band - loose on her ring finger. She looks like a child wearing their mother's jewelry. I lose it.

I spin on the director and tell him,

"This is going to be a closed casket!"

Relief crosses his brow. He tells me with a closed casket loved ones will put large pictures of the deceased on easels next to the casket, so people can remember her when she was healthy. I ask him for a moment alone with her. I kneel next to her, me leaning against her shoulder.

"This wasn't what we planned baby. We never got to Europe; we never got the sun porch done, and YOU WERE SUPPOSED TO BE WITH ME FOREVER! What am I going to do now? I am all alone – I miss you!"

I cry and cry and cry. These are pitiful, selfish tears. I think I am all out of pain, here's a new one: loneliness.

It takes me five minutes, copious amounts of spit and a lot of pain to get off my wedding ring. It has not budged from my finger in 18 years. Twenty pounds later my finger has swelled around the ring like a large tree growing through a cyclone fence. When I finally tug it off, it flies from my hand. I hear it make that ping noise a coin makes when flipped properly, then a metallic ding, hitting the leg of the gurney she was on. I fell to the ground searching for it. It dawns on me that this is the second time today I am on the ground looking for something that doesn't exist anymore. There's a numbing that occurs when you are lying on a cold, ceramic floor in a funeral fuckatorium, at the foot of a dead person they keep telling you is your wife.

I want to lay there until I die. I rest my cheek on the floor. The coolness of the tiles actually felt good. It seems like the right place to die: a funeral home. When I locate the ring, I notice that my ring fit better now on my pinky. This is not my wedding ring. Wedding rings go on ring fingers given to you by people who love you and are not dead!

I pull myself to my knees and then walk on my knees to the edge of the gurney. I put my ring on her middle finger next to her rings on her forth finger. I stare at it for awhile. I cannot look at her lifeless, brown, clown face. I focus on our rings, the only things that still shine. Our rings. Our love. My pain. My hatred. I place my hand on hers. I feel our rings on her fingers. I say…

"Goodbye, I love you."

…one last time, motion for the director get me out of this evil room with strict instruction to keep the casket closed, then left.

6

You want to have a fucked day?
Spend your wife's 40th birthday in a cancer ward
surprised she reached 40.

I head home through the park, then through the city -
anything to fill time away from the house, crossing through
downtown and son of a bitch! I see my favorite homeless guy
talking to a handful of other homeless guys, splitting a bottle of
some alcoholic piss. It is absurd but I almost expect to see him,
now somewhere. There is a numbness that occurs when you have
lost your best friend, and you are lonely and broken hearted. You
feel like you are trapped in a bad Hitchcock movie. Seeing him
proves one of two things: He isn't really there and I am going
crazy or he is actually following me around town and I am going
crazy. I don't even care that he was there. I didn't care about
anything anymore. Enjoy your fucked up life, enjoy your hooch,
my homeless hallucination. Today I don't even give a fuck
because your life is better than mine.

I actually feel surly. I like the emotional variation because
it feels better than sadness. Hate is the only thing left, and if
someone wants some, I can deliver. My homeless guy sees me and
starts scrambling around shopping carts full of homeless
possessions. I know what he was looking for. He can't find the
sign! He becomes agitated and starts flinging anything he can get

his hands on. I, on the other hand, find immeasurable joy in his inability to produce his placard.

One of his drinking buddies is using the now tattered sign as a mattress to separate his body from the hot aluminum street bench. My homeless guy pulls out the corner of the sign from under the sleeping drunk, and with a magicians skill, flips him from back to belly like a hamburger on a barbeque. I pass by him, relishing the moment in which he cannot flash me his stupid sign. In my rearview mirror I see him running toward me. He takes three large, running, steps and Frisbees the sign in my direction. I am watching this placard flying toward me when the wind takes it in another direction and is now flipping end over end. With every flip I see the message: TALK TO GOD. Flip: TALK TO GOD. Flip: TALK TO GOD.

He cannot know the immense pain I am in. If he did, neither he nor anyone else would mess with a guy the week his wife has died. Or would he? Maybe I should talk to God. How about a few Hail Marys? Would you feel better, God? Can you hear me, God? Fuck you God!

The last time we tried God was after the final round of chemotherapy failed to stop the cancer. We went to our church: we prayed and cried and even spent a few moments with our priest. We all prayed together and then he told us that God works in mysterious ways. He said that there is a greater plan for all of us, and that this was God's will. Then he ended on a good note: My wife and I will be rejoined in heaven for eternity. Imagine that: saying to a woman who will be dead in less than a month that she and I will be in heaven for eternity. Fuck him! Where is she now!

All this coming from a guy whose bosses financed the largest pedophile ring the United States had ever known. Fuck him!
I now wonder if these diddling ass bags will be in heaven: Who will they rejoin? And, if they are in heaven, do they have to register their cloud at the pearly gates since they are known and convicted sex offenders? Or since they were priests on earth, do they get a string of male cherubs to fuck all day non-

stop? There is numbness that occurs when you hear someone say something so stupid that your brain wanders off to dastardly places.

I remember thinking, I want all three of us dead. My bride, so her pain will end; me, assuming the priest was right, so we could go back to just being us on some cloud in heaven; and the priest, for being such a dumb ass for saying such a fucked up thing. If you want me to talk to God, my homeless hallucination, he has to answer for taking my wife.

One thing I am unaware of is that funeral homes have more than one funeral going on at a time. It takes me a few hours to figure out that half the people I see in the common areas are of no relation to me or my wife. They are just going to the funeral down the hall. The only other time I can remember a set-up like this was at our wedding. There were three wedding receptions in this huge hall that night. Toward the end of the evening you would see people at "our" reception with different tuxedos, and different bridesmaid's dresses, dancing, laughing, and drinking with people from our wedding. I guess they came from a dry wedding down the hall or liked our D.J. better. And as quick as a song would end, they all would run down to the other hall looking for the better song or a bar that was staying open longer. What joy! What fun! You would walk to the restroom through the main hallway and you couldn't help but think that the tuxedo shop and the formal dress store have made a killing that night.

I wonder why they don't do that at funeral homes. A true celebration of someone's life. I should have gotten a D.J. and hosted an open bar. Everybody puts on a tuxedo or an evening gown, gets drunk and dances. I totally missed that one. Instead we have whispers, wailing, endless tears.

I witness six funerals or parts thereof while at the funeral home. What I do learn in time is that funerals are for old people. There is an expected and accepted length to a human's life. If a person dies in their 90's, most of the people who know and love them are gone or not at the services because they are too old to travel. The only way they will get to a funeral home is feet first.

37

People at the funeral say she lived a long and happy life. Usually by the time you reach your 90's you are not too sure how old you are - the perfect time to die.

The 80's I would call a "solid length." No surprises when you go. The family is sad but they say things like: "Boy he sure looks good," and "He was 87; he doesn't even look 75." The 70's are still well within the death acceptance curve. You get a few more, "Gosh, I just talked to him yesterday," and "What a surprise." There are more kids at the funeral around this age because it is usually a Grandma or Grandpa. You see the little people dressed up like big people, parading through the halls looking to do anything except go in and see their dead grandpa. The whole idea of a little person getting dragged to a funeral and having to be put through that ordeal is jacked. There will be plenty of dysfunctional parents screwing up their lives for the next 20 years, why start the nightmares early? Can't they just let them remember them alive? I am trying.

Now with death in the 60's you are getting into some pain. People the same age arrive with that "That could have been me", shit my pants, look on their faces, comparing their fucked up health to the guy in the box up front. Usually there are some teen kids around if he held out for a trophy wife or traded in the old one for the newer model. But for sure there are young adults with strollers and babies. There are plenty of tears you drop in this age bracket.

The 50's: the 50's are tough. This is usually a dad with a surprise death; dropped dead from a heart attack or hit by a car type death leading this category. You now have a widow with teen kids, the mortgage, and her ass is too big to hook another sucker, so her life is truly fucked.

We were in the 40's bracket by just two months. She said she was going to stay 39 for ten years, just keep telling people she was 39 when asked. And I know she could have pulled it off. She actually stayed 39 for about five months then cancer took her to 99 in three more.

She had her 40th birthday in the hospital. You want to
have a fucked day? Spend your wife's 40th birthday in a cancer
ward surprised she reached 40. That's what we celebrated: her
living until her fortieth birthday. No surprise party for her.

That was a hard day; pumped full of chemo kryptonite,
tired, vomiting bile, no appetite, she could barely keep her eyes
open. Her favorite cake from Hodell's Pastries sits untouched on
the rolling tray table at the foot of the bed. I am starving but
would never think about having a piece if she couldn't share it
with me.

The morning turns into a hot afternoon. She is asleep
and exhausted. The intense sunlight through the window feels
good on my face, but begins melting her beautiful cake. Her name
is scrolled on the top in pink; ha the yellow and green sugar roses
and the bunting made of frosting start to melt into psychedelic
goo. The icing is falling off the sides, exposing the cherry nut
cake. The cherries and nuts look awful in the blistering sun.
Within an hour the cake actually starts to list. I sit there in my
uncomfortable chair and watch her cake and her body deteriorate
at about the same speed.

There is a numbing that occurs when you have to buy a
birthday gift for the love of your life who is about to die. You
need to be very careful. Buy anything with any utility beyond one
or two days, and everyone starts to cry. Buy a gift with too much
emotional value, and everyone starts to cry. Buy a gift that
requires being out of the hospital to enjoy it, and everyone starts
crying.

I would recommend flowers. There is a slim chance she
will outlive them, and a woman, dying or not, always loves her
favorite flowers. Ours were roses. When I got my visa bill a
month after she had died I saw that I purchased 64 dozen roses. I
betcha that florist was sad to see her go.

From 40 years old and younger, death and the funeral
are comprised of pure, palpable pain. Young people are not
supposed to die, and their families are not supposed to spend

three days at a funeral home crying. There must have been some colossal accident; a drunk driver, house fire, leukemia - but to be dead in the prime of your life is tragic for everyone. Funerals for the young sting; they leave scars and take months, maybe years, to get over. Funerals are for old people.

Hour after hour for two days I stand alone in the back and receive family and friends offering their condolences. I find myself comforting more than being comforted. I was the one that witnessed her erosion. These folks, especially the ones from out of town, only remember her when she was alive and full of life. They all meant well – I guess. I don't really care.

My homeless, sign toting hallucination shows up at the funeral home on the second day. He stands across the street with his sign. I would occasionally peer through the sheer drapes to see if he has left. I figure he was there for three hours until one of the other families complained to the funeral director. The police arrive and asked him to leave. He doesn't go right away. The police park their cruiser between him and the funeral home until he is finally escorted away in the squad car.

I am questioned by a number of people as to why the casket was closed. I want to tell them that the bad stunt double mannequin, in the coffin playing the part of my dead wife, would horrify most of the people who knew her. The photos, enlarged and mounted on foam core from Kinkos or Fed Ex Office, fuck it; Finkos, are displayed next to the coffin, would be a better image to take with them than what remains in that box. In hindsight, I think I might have kept the coffin open so people could see she was really dead. As it was, they had to take my word for it. Oddly I feel more pressure to explain. I think if they would have seen her I wouldn't have had to talk so much. I take from the experience the satisfaction of knowing I kept all their memories pristine.

Before the funeral home opens for the first day of viewing, her parents find out I decided to keep the casket closed. They are upset with my decision and want to see her. It makes total sense, and I actually expect it. I leave the room. I have said my goodbyes the night before. When I came back into the viewing area he doesn't say another word about open or closed casket. Her mom is going into shock. I motion for the funeral director to call 911. She crumples into a heap in her husband's arms. I quickly grab the other side of her body. She is not supporting any of her weight. I glance into his eyes, and see he is about to collapse too. He is flop sweating and his knees are crumpling in half. I know that look. I have seen it in the mirror for the last eight months. It feels as if I am supporting all of us. That was never my thing; that was always hers. She supported all of us, and now she is not here to help, just me: Mr. Dumbass! Fuck!

We all fall into one of those gaudy, overstuffed, red, gothic, sofas you only find in funeral homes, a pile of broken hearted humanity. We cannot let each other go. We cry and cry; our hearts forever broken, hollowed out and filled in with black fucking cement. Any three of us would have given our lives for her to be able to keep living.

7

We had the three-course iron maiden.
They bombed her with the crap,
amputated her perfect breasts, and then she died.

There is a hollowness that occurs when someone you love is gone: like stumbling through a blackened room searching for a lightswitch with your hands in front of your face, never finding the light. Will it ever end? The house is sold in a matter of days. She was Mrs. Curb Appeal. We had always planned to sell it and get something in the country. So much for plans.

Her sister and mom come into town to help me go through her things as soon as they hear I am selling the place. They fill a bunch of shipping boxes with memories. I don't think much of it. I am not upset about it and don't jockey for anything they want to take. If you would have asked me I would have thrown it all out. They did their best to tiptoe around my feelings, what they think I would want before they latch onto it. After a few pale requests they realize I am amicable, yielding to all their inquiries. They stop asking.

Her sister comes out of the bedroom with a suggestion. Surprised that I plan to sell the furniture and not keep it for memory's sake, she thinks selling it and donating the proceeds to the Susan G. Komen Breast Cancer charity would be something

42

her sister would have wanted. Maybe more of us should have peddled our furniture years ago to cure cancer. We wouldn't have anything to sit on, but she still might be alive. I fake smile and think that is a wonderful suggestion and promise to make a phone call the next day.

As I now wander emotionally rudderless into my mid-40's my mind drifts to my childhood when I was in second grade. I remember asking my mom if I could try to stay up for 24 hours straight to watch Jerry Lewis and Ed McMahan raise money for Muscular Dystrophy on the Labor Day weekend telethon. Every year people would donate millions of dollars to fight MD. To a young boy, the millions seemed like more money than anyone would ever need to cure anything. The dollars piled up and up. I figured with that kind of money a cure was right around the corner! The band would strike up every time the tote board was ready to roll over to a new and amazing dollar figure, always breaking last year's total and, of course, surpassing the goal.

Stars from television and movies would be on the show singing and dancing. I thought with this kind of money they for sure would cure MD this year. That was 36 years ago. I guess the show still airs on some cable network. I stopped watching a few years later because after all the money that was collected – even my Christmas money one year from my Aunt Pudge - still no cure. I wondered what they did with all that money. If Rip Taylor is still on the show, I think I may tune in again. Is he alive? Did he die? Did he die of MD?

I guess cancer has gotten better to have now, but there is no cure, no shot, no antibiotic. What they know is if you keep checking yourself for cancer, and they find it early enough they can kill it by pumping you full of shit only made by a nuclear reactor "or" and this is a big "or," removing that body part before the cancer spreads into places that you can't remove without dying.

They have gotten better at the radiation assaults on your body. They built a better gun, a smart bomb that hits the cancer plagued areas with less collateral damage. Ha! Ask someone who has been through it. We had the three-course iron maiden: They bombed her with the crap, amputated her perfect breasts, then she died. We didn't get to dessert; the cure – which there is none to date. The cure for cancer is just fucking removing the part of the body.   That's the cure. Cure is the wrong word. Subtraction, dismemberment, amputation, death, and destruction - those are the words that describe the present "cure" for cancer. Fuck it.

If you haven't had the pleasure of getting involved in some of the cancer charities or cancer walk events, you should get involved and evaluate the programs and charities before your sister, mom, or wife is dying and before you get sucked into that hellish process. The funny thing is: You never want to even get close to any of it in fear of jinxing your healthy life. You never want to press your luck, screw up your karma, or jack up your chi, so you don't get involved until you have a wife with cancer and you are a blubbering ball of tears. Then you spend the remaining months of her life surrounding yourself with survivors who were dealt a worse hand than you so you can compare T cell counts and sleep another night knowing there is someone else out there who has had it worse and survived.

After you get the news you are fucked. You start looking for emotional lifeboats, upbeat survivors, and the percentages of success of your particular cancer. You start at your doctor's office, then head to the internet and immerse yourself in the pink world of the fucked. Diet, exercise, and lifestyle choices are now all relevant. "Your cancer, with early detection, gives you a rate of survival of 92%." Hell, we can live with that! Let's go to dinner.

Search the web for any cancer information and you are sure to find yourself at the doorstep of a cancer charity. There are the fundraising walks where they amass thousands of destroyed souls to bleed them out on booming speakers systems, each with a story of how their loved one passed, and always ending with how important it is to "find a cure" - or find your wallet. One after another, mothers of daughters, husbands of wives, daughters of mothers pour their guts out all over again to thousands of other lost souls treading in water from a nuclear reactor rod cooling tank, in the land of the pink chemo-fucked. These charity events are the scab that keeps getting knocked off and bleeds endlessly.

The people that run these charities are all business and little cancer; emotions probably callused over by making a living hustling broken souls. There is a shrewdness to these people, a business approach to the events. I didn't say "hustle" but "business approach." I guess the story goes that there was a daughter who lost a mother a long time ago, and she started the charity my wife's sister wanted me to donate every stick of furniture to.

You didn't hear any more pain in her voice at the microphone. She was all business.

"You need to make sure you have your donor card filled out with the proper bank information in box six before you receive your wristband and t-shirt."

I've seen enough of those fucking snap-on wristbands. You know you are in trouble and have been in the hospital too long when they have to change your wristband because it is stained with sweat, blood, bile, and death. When they stop typing your allergies on it and all it reads is "morpheme all day and all night," you know you are on your last wristband.

"Make sure you sign the back of the card if you haven't already done it on our web site so we can automatically deposit your donation – before we start curing cancer this morning."

The charity's web site is a financial juggernaut that would be the envy of the largest banks in the world. Make a donation; click here. Purchase a pink hat or pink T-shirt; click here. Donate money; click here. Donate money; click there. A big pink hankie to mop up your money and tears; click here. No buckets of one-dollar bills from Rip Taylor here. This is professional fundraising.

More tanned, well heeled looking people pull up in very large tour buses with big titles. They are dressed well, with that look of money. They speak next, a report from the front, an update on how the war on cancer is going. Their message is similar to the one before. The public address system booms:

"Money cures cancer." "You miss your wife? Write a check!"

To participate you usually need to get a couple thousand dollars in donations before you can spend a day or two or three walking a ton of miles for "The Cure." No cure for us. We probably didn't get enough donations to get the good medicine. I did get a T-shirt. I threw that fucker out first. I couldn't help thinking that with all these people walking and paying and paying and paying: How much money really goes to the doctors? How much money is funneled to the hospital where my wife died? How much does it cost to buy that fancy pink tour bus?

The last person to speak is The Cancer Walk Master of Ceremonies: a twisted retread from the 1960s game show era, including the bad Rip Taylor toupee and a tuxedo with blue sparkles. Pink is the color here, pal. He is the "walk motivator," I guess. This is the guy who sings a bit, says all the right things, gets all the women revved up, and just before he finishes, points his finger, cueing the sound board operator. Sorry, no orchestra here today, all the money is funneled directly to research. The song, "Don't Stop Believing" by Journey, blares through the giant speakers; everyone cheers and the Baton Death March begins. He reminds me of Jerry Lewis, the wasted five dollars I got from my Aunt Pudge, and now they get my furniture.

I have what I want to keep: the photos from the kitchen floor, our wedding pictures, the twisted red straws, our vacation videos, a number of ticket stubs we kept, and her laptop. I toss it all into a box a little bigger than a case of beer, and I mean tossed, with no form or order. This is so me and so not her. I like that. I tape the box shut with some of that industrial strength moving tape, the kind that makes that horrible screeching noise when you press it around the box from the hand dispenser, round and round I keep circling the box with the tape: left to right, up and back, over and over until the tape: is gone. Nearly every inch of the box was covered high gloss, extra-heavy-strength packing tape. I would need a blow torch to open it up again. I write today's date on it, curious as to how long it would take until I had the will, the fortitude and the energy to ever open it up again.

I help the gals pack their car up. They cannot get that "thieves in the night" look off their faces for some reason; it is probably just me over accessing. We don't have anything of real value, but they found enough of her stuff that they wanted to fill up a minivan. I am sure if I ever want to look at any of her things they would let me come over.

We did the fake cheek kiss and the barely touching hug thing. Her mom tells me to "stay in touch," but I know at that moment I will never see them again. Why would they want to see me? We are actors living out a Greek tragedy, and I have the part, in their minds, of Thespis, the Greek Father of Tragedy. No one invites tragedy over for dinner.

I send the good furniture to an auction house and Goodwill backs a truck up and finishes the job. They are happy. The jury is still out as to whether I plan on sending the pink army my profits from the furniture sale supporting the cure that doesn't cure.

8

You want me to talk to God? I'll talk to God!
I'll send you to Him you motherfucker! Here I am!

Days and weeks started meshing together into a dull,
gray ooze. The apartment I take by work affords little creature
comforts, but I like it that way because it is free from memories. It
is painfully simple: In the front room is a reclining chair I bought
at the Goodwill. I find one of those crappy TV tables made out of
the cheapest tin, in the alley behind the apartment complex, with
the snap legs that always pinch your fingers and tasteless flower
art on the tabletop surface. It bows at the top of the table, would
flex back and forth depending on what you put on it and where.
My hassock is the beer case sized box entombed in an entire roll
of packing tape. Stationed on the right side of the recliner, I live
off this table: car keys, wallet, and the evening's takeout fare. I do
spring for a flat screen television and cable. I haven't figured out
the stand, like I give a fuck, so it leans against the wall. I feel I owe
myself a window to the world. It was that TV or a case of Jack
Daniels and a loaded fire arm. The flat screen is less messy.

There is nothing in the kitchen nook in the way of table
or chairs, nothing in the kitchen drawers. My utensils: made of
plastic and delivered with each Styrofoam entree, are wrapped in
cellophane and are tossed after each takeout meal. Short of a trash

bin in the kitchen, left by the prior tenants, the area is off limits. That was her room.

I buy an overnight travel kit for my bathroom needs: little miniature deodorant, cologne, hair gel, toothpaste and a tooth brush with a small handle. I think about getting the adult size stuff, but the trip to the corner drugstore every week is a nice break in the boredom.

I stop buying my cologne that I have been using since I was 14. I can't put it on any longer; it acts like a trigger for memories of her. It begins to nauseate me. Her perfume of choice was Armani's "Code." It's sexy, light, and delicious. Now, when I pass a woman wearing it, I lurch with a flood of emotions. I used to begin tearing up, but now when I smell it my mouth gets dry, my pulse races, and I get a headache like someone hit me in the back of the head with a two by four. Fuck.

I buy a small, cheap twin bed. It feels penitentiary firm, and since I have no flare for making a bed, I wake up in the middle of the night with the mattress sheet at my feet and my face pressed into one of those mattress buttons that hold the mattress together. I couldn't stand a two person bed. I have made plans to purchase a pillow and learn how to do a load of laundry.

There is a hollowness that occurs when someone you love is gone. Holidays become Tuesdays; big family, three-day weekends are spent at work. I figure I owe them for the mountain of time I missed. I hated to sleep just until lately. I frequently dream we are together. She is alive, and we are doing something menial: cleaning out the garage or shopping at one of those Hallmark stores full of stuff that is really cute but no one needs. I can feel the warmth well up through me. I feel myself impulsively adjust my body to my perfect and most comfortable sleeping position to extend the dream. I feel the ends of my mouth turn-up and smile. Am I alive? Am I dead? Wherever I am, I am with her, and I like it.

There is a horrible realization that comes when my dream ends and my twin-bed reality wakes me up and slaps me in the face. I am alone. At first I hate these dreams because of the tragic ending that comes with consciousness. Over time, I have grown to appreciate and enjoy the memories. It has allowed me to look forward to sleep and to start remembering her without excruciating pain.

The other good news is that I have stopped hallucinating; at least I think I did. It has been three months since I have seen my TALK TO GOD homeless man - roughly the same period of time since she passed. I thought I saw him once at a mall talking to a bunch of teens, but was not positive. I didn't see a sign, and he sure didn't chase me. So I think that in my cancer haze he was probably just a loon with bad timing or a frequent figment of my pickled imagination...until this morning at work.

What the fuck? Through the tinted windows in the building next to ours, stands the homeless man, dressed the same as every other time I've seen him, holding the sign. He is staring at me, nodding his head, smiling, and pointing to his sign. It is creepy. Now the unique thing about my building with the green tinted glass is things from the outside or from his perspective in the building across the parking lot, you can see out of my building but you can't see in. The building he is standing in had that 1970's, two-way, thinly smoked glass windows so we can always see in. We make fun of how we can keep an eye on all their activities when all they can see is the emerald city of mirrors on our side.

It was pure soap-opera comedy two summers before when one of the offices turned into a lover's triangle that played out in front of most of the people on our floor. The big female exec was nailing two different male interns in her office who both worked on her floor, one on each side of her office. She had them both by fifty pounds. I am surprised she never thought we could see in. Someone from security in our building alerted people over there that the live sex shows were becoming distracting. Three days later she had vertical blinds installed. A few months later the company moved her and her sexual appetite for male interns to bigger digs a of couple miles away, leaving the sixth-floor offices vacant. I am sure she had blinds installed immediately in her new office.

With the emerald mirror exterior how can my hallucination see me? How does he know where I am so he could be directly across from me? And how does he manage to get into those empty offices? Proof: I am seeing things and near crazy. Did I change my meds? Why is he back? Fuck! But there he is: my homeless guy, six floors up in the sexual romping offices directly across from my cube, staring at me through emerald glass you cannot see through. Shit! I had thought I was feeling better but no, not now; clearly still having episodes.

I leap from my chair and go to the restroom to splash some water on my face. My pulse rate soars. I start sweating. I feel lightheaded. Where's my aspirin? If I am having a heart attack I want a shot at saving myself. No aspirin. Shit! This is a full mental breakdown, but I have been feeling better lately. I douse my face again with two full handfuls of cold water. I look at myself in the mirror: what a fucking wreck, I actually say aloud.

"Hold on man you are just suffering."

Great, I am now talking to myself.

"The guy is not real, and for sure he is not there."

I wait for what seems ten minutes and head back to my cube. I don't look in the direction of my window. I don't dare. I start doing anything and everything I can at my desk to keep my head down: busy, busy, busy. I align my ass awkwardly in my chair so I can't see my window with my peripheral vision. Fuck! Is he still there? I feel the sweat filling my armpits and the crack of my ass.

I take a call from our east coast auditor about an outstanding invoice. Peter has been a good, long-distance friend through the cancer. He isn't a big talker and for some reason knows not to ask how I am doing? In fact, he seems to have the wherewithal to talk about anything but cancer. He is a good phone friend whom I hope to meet someday. As he presses me for who I think will win the NBA's Eastern Conference this year, Christine, the woman I share a cube wall with, cranes her neck around the corner as she usually does with juicy office gossip and says,

"Sorry to interrupt, but do you see that man over there? I think he is trying to get your attention?"

Without looking toward the window, I reply.

"So, you see him?"

"Of course I see him, but I can't figure out how he is seeing you. You can't see with the green, one way gla-...."

And before she can finish her thought, I quickly tell Peter I am going to call him back, slam down the phone and bolt for the door. It is time to end this shit, real or not. I am through with this. This assbag is now going to come up against my will.

Rage replaces fear. Through the office entryway and into the elevator I bound. My madness is ratcheting up. It feels good. I have a target for my pain, and I hope he is real. Out the front doors of the building I fly, rolling up my sleeves like someone preparing to brawl. Leaving my building, looking back I verify what I know: you can't see into my building, only reflections of a madman storming across the lawn ready to attack what now has become the new face of my pain - or at least verify that I have gone around the bend and need lithium.

I move quickly to the elevator of the building next door. The cafeteria for the entire office complex is in this building, so I am familiar with its layout. Up the elevator and out onto floor six. I actually start jogging down the hallway toward the offices that face mine. I want to surprise him, but for sure get to him before he sneaks off or vaporizes into my psyche.

"You want me to talk to God? I'll talk to God! I'll send you to Him you mother fucker! Here I am!"

I get to the door, snap down the handle and shoulder the door for my big entrance. Thud! My shoulder mashes against the door and it does not give. It is locked. I try it again, and again. I can't get the door open. Fuck! I race down the hall to the next available entrance to the large, empty space across from mine: again locked. There is no way in, and when I peer through the small vertical window next to the door, I see nothing in the office suite where he just was and where all the trysts took place. Is this the right door? Is this the right floor? Fuck! Fuck! Fuck! This is total bullshit! I am now consumed with anger and fear. No homeless man exists and therefore it is undeniable verification that I am a nut!

"No, this can't be! FUCK!"

I circle the entire floor and then the floors below looking for this guy. I turn up nothing. I ask the security guard at the front desk if he has seen a man that fits my guy's description; nothing. I tell him I think I saw this guy from my office next door up on floor six. And before he can explain how one way windows work to me, I stop him. Then he verifies that there is no company leasing the space on six right now.

"They left months ago and the floor is empty."

Soaked with sweat and getting used to the idea that I am totally certifiable, I go back to my office. I am pissed and probably look like a fool to anyone who saw me running out of the building like it was on fire. When I arrive back at my cube, Christine asks me if I have spoken to the guy. Between panting, holding my side, and inhaling huge gulps of air I tell her,

"No, I couldn't find him."

Voice wobbly, timid and a bit startled, she whispers softy as not to be heard.

"He is back there."

9

Where are you going? You are alone.
You have nowhere to go and no one to go home to.
You eat alone; you sleep alone; you have nothing.
Your wife is gone.

After Christine confirms my worst fears, I look over and my homeless hallucination is right where I saw him the first time on the sixth floor, only now he's waving at me to come over, pointing to his TALK TO GOD sign, and I can see that the locked door to the hallway is now propped wide open with an office garbage can. I must have had the wrong floor. I step to my window, stare right at him, and mouth: You want to fuck with me? Thumbs indicating myself, sassy but mean. He grins, nods his approval, and points to the sign. Then he gives me another wave over. Man, this is bullshit! Christine asks if she should call the cops or if I was going back over there? And before the words leave her mouth I am on my way back there, more pissed than before.

I don't remember crossing the "green space" that separates our buildings. I do remember passing by the security guard who, when he sees the look of demonic possession on my face, tries to stop me. I keep thinking: so this is how crazy people act. Don't remember if I take the stairs or the elevator. I think I am losing consciousness. Fuck it. This guy is mine!

Adrenalin is pumping through my veins like battery acid. Drenched in sweat and hate from hair to heel, I get to the same door on six, no propped door with garbage can, so with all my rage and fury I slam the door handle downward flinging myself against the oak door, half of me thinking that it is not going to budge again and my shoulder would press against it in vain like day old mashed potatoes. Surprisingly, the door handle clicks, and I find myself off my feet, riding the swing of the large oak door, then jettisoning in full flight into the middle of an empty office area half the length of a football field. I land on my keys. Fuck, that hurt! I try to get to my feet. I am a raging, pile of pain, sorrow, and sadness. I never thought I could ever evolve into this type of a subhuman. I am breathless, simpleminded - and seething.

I crouch low into a track runner's starting position. I survey the room; a hungry beast, scanning for prey. I raise my head looking through my sweat, wet hair dangling, obscuring my view. And there he is: my hallucination staring at me and smiling. He and I with nothing between us but 30 yards of used indoor-faded, shit-blue office carpet. I scream:

"What is your fucking problem? Why can't you leave me alone?"

No response; just a shit eating smile. I get to my feet, feeling a bit lightheaded, my ass hurting where my keys stuck me. I begin moving toward him walking fast, but I know the final three steps I am full out running! My old football instincts kick in: stay low, engage at the chest, and drive through your man. My hands hit him right on the numbers: good form. Keeping my legs moving and my feet under my weight, I grab onto the unzipped sides of his army jacket. So he was real. Upon impact, the TALK TO GOD sign is knocked from his hand, spins a few times in midair and rocks to the floor like a kite struggling to keep the wind under it. I drive him back quickly, his feet moving fast with mine so he won't fall. My shoulder lodged against his chest, my head to the side, ear pressed against his rib cage. He is gasping.

The blow must have knocked the wind out of him. Good! Motherfucker!

After about five strides together we hit the wall, his head then his shoulders: POW! My nose crushes against his jacket. He smells of urine and sleeping outdoors. It was gagging. There was so much sleeping-in-dumpsters soot on his jeans that they had taken on a shiny veneer. With my head under his arm, I see he is wearing two different shoes: one an old black, army boot missing the tongue, with no sock; the other a women's old rubber gym shoe you would expect to see on your grandmother; the kind they sell at K-mart for seven dollars.

The force of both of us cracks the drywall on impact. Dust from the rattled ceiling tiles creates a white cloud of dust falling down on our heads. I wrap my right arm around him so he has no use of his left arm. My left forearm is pressing under his chin and my hand presses against his mouth.

I start driving my shoulder into his midsection. I want to push this guy through the wall. Over and over again I keep throwing every bit of strength and energy into crushing this guy, all the time screaming at him:

"Leave me alone you fucking asshole. Leave (bang) me, (bang) the fuck (bang) alone (bang) you fucking (bang) asshole (bang). Leave (bang) me, (bang) the fuck (bang) alone (bang) you fucking (bang) assbag! (bang)."

What little resistance I felt earlier has left his body, and I am now supporting his weight as he remains pinned against the wall. What the fuck am I doing? I am now certifiably mad. I am attacking a homeless man in an empty office building and am probably being watched by all my co-workers. First a sex addict she-whale and now me: a lunatic terminator beating, and I mean pounding, a bum. Fuck! Stop. It took everything that was left of my commonsense to stop pummeling this guy.

I rock back withdrawing my shoulder from his midsection but never taking my elbow and hand from his chin. I lift my head. His eyes are closed, fear and humiliation on his brow, body quivering and face wincing, awaiting my next shoulder blow to his midsection. I relax. He feels me recoiling out of exhaustion. I am now looking at his closed eyes, face to face, one inch apart, my hand mashing his lips against his teeth and my fingers twisting his nose like a child squeezing play-doh through their fingers.

Slowly, with the steadiness and pace of an electric garage door opening, his eyelids begin parting, initially tacky and slowed by sweat and eye discharge. I see the strain in the thin skin of his eyelids trying to separate. They quiver, needing a good rub, but I do not afford him the use of his hands. Long, sun soaked eyelids glistening with tears from the pain are now the only thing keeping his eyes from opening. With a forced blink his eyelids separate, first the left then the right. Now eye to eye, separated by one inch of space and air, I am panting into his face staring into his eyes.

I expect a lunatic haze, or bloodshot, hungover, whiskey-pickled eyes: They are nothing of the sort. Instead they are calm and confident, crystal Caribbean blue, the same color of my wife's caring, loving, with not one, red, road mapped vein cluttering the purity of the whites of his eyes. I stare hard into them. They are exactly the same as my wife's. It startles me then frightens me. They cut right through me. Now I know he and I are both crazy. No one takes that kind of abuse and enjoys it. Shaken, I ease the death grip under his chin, mouth, and nose just enough to allow his face to snap back. He breaks into a warm greeting smile. What the fuck?

My rage escalates again.

"What is your problem? Why the fuck are you following me? Leave me the FUCK ALONE. Do you hear me; can you hear me?"

I bang his body one last time into the now cracked and dented drywall. I have run out of strength and adrenalin. I lean against him, exhausted, gasping for air and without a plan. Now what? What I know for sure is that I am not ready to let him go. Surprising me, he then puts his free hand around my back to support my weight. We stand there staring into each other's eyes, worn out, panting, him smiling and me broken hearted, soulless, and ready to cry.

Oddly, I don't want to move, and it seems neither does he. So we just stay, leaning against each other, both trying to catch our breath. His hypnotic stare is riveting. My hand still presses against his mouth, but with less force. I feel his mouth move, spread his lips, and lick them, cleaning away the dust from the ceiling, some dried egg from who knows what and dirt. I pull my hand from his mouth and nose and rest it on his chin, wincing as he grabs his first full breath since my attack. He stares into my eyes and speaks.

"Do you want to talk to God?"

Too exhausted to hit him again, too freaked about his eyes, too emotionally frazzled to give a shit, I blurt out a sarcastically:

"Ha!"

I put my index finger to his mouth, shaking my head "no" and shushing him.

"There is no God in my world. What do you want me to do? Go to church? Stare at a cross? I said a lifetime of prayers, cried a million tears, and 'GOD!' still took my wife from me. I really don't care to talk to the fucking asshole today, pal, or any other day. What the fuck am I doing here?"

He leans his head back into the concave impression the back of his head has made in the drywall, gaining separation from my index finger. He smiles and begins to speak slowly, his voice like warm butterscotch caramel.

"Not God nor anyone else took your wife. God didn't have a plan for her. God doesn't work in mysterious ways. Your wife's body could no longer sustain her, she had to move on. I will tell you she is fine, happy and in a wonderful place."

Rage! Screaming now!

"What the FUCK do you know about my wife? SHE IS DEAD! SHE IS FUCKING DEAD! SHE IS GONE. You've got to leave me alone! You fuck with me and my memories, I swear I will kill you!"

I slip out of our exhausted hug and push him back against the wall with one hand, teeing him up to swing at him with the other, trying to summon enough energy to raise my arm and ball my fist. But I am spent. I fall back into him, broken, sliding down his chest to his belt buckle, to my knees, sobbing and screaming:

"She is gone! She is FUCKING DEAD! She is GONE! SHE IS DEAD! DON'T YOU FUCKING UNDERSTAND?"

I reach up to pound on his chest, but can only afford the strength to raise my hand. Tears pour from my eyes. Snot runs from my nose. I cry like I did the day we found out there was no cure and it was only a matter of time. Bawling, I fall back away from him on my knees, then sitting on my heels, I bury my head in my hands and weep uncontrollably.

"I promise you if you talk to God it will help you."

I raise my head from my hands in submission.

"What, do you want from me? Are you fucking hustling me? Is this a shakedown for money? Well, forget it, I am broke. Your God gave my wife an expensive disease that wasn't totally covered under my co-pay. She's gone, but her bills are still here asshole! Why don't you have your God help pay my bills, dickhead?"

Done, cried out, and in pain from throttling this person, I am ready to leave. I need to get back to work, go home, or find a bar. I have had enough of this freak. I get to my feet and mumble something about killing him if he ever gets near me again meshed with some bullshit about restraining orders I picked up on "CSI Miami". I dry my red, swollen eyes, this after swearing I would never cry again, turn my back to him and start walking away.

Talk to God

"If you know God give him this for me you fuck."

I flip him off. Nice touch, huh?

"I am God."

"You are a deranged fuck my friend. Fuck square off you fucking fuck. You are not God. You are a homeless psychopath living in a dumpster or in some refrigerator box. You are a fucking loon who seems to like to follow suffering people and fuck with them - probably for money."

His timbre and conviction doesn't change.

"I give you my word. I swear….."

I am still walking away, my back to him, with at least thirty feet separating us.

"Were you about to say: 'swear to God' or better yet, 'swear to you'? You are more fucked up than I am, pal. Find help you, homeless prick and take a fucking shower! You stink like the god of shit!"

"What do you have to lose? You've lost everything else, and now you think you are losing your mind."

That religious, fucking prick! I wheel around and wave my right index finger at him.

"Another fucking word out of you, freak, and you'll wish you never woke up on the sidewalk this morning,- ASSHOLE."

His facial expression doesn't change: confident with a friendly smile.

"Where are you going? You are alone. You have nowhere to go, and no one to go home to. You eat alone; you sleep alone; you have nothing. Your wife is gone."

That does it. I charge him.

"Okay, God, wanna talk? Let's talk!"

60

A few long, fast strides and I am back on him. Fuck the fact that his eyes look like my wife's - coincidence. I have never fought anyone before. I mean, I scrapped in elementary school, but never boxed, so I was about to navigate uncharted waters.

"You want to talk to me, motherfucker?"

I grab him by the shirt and reach back with my right hand, ball my fist, and start this long, telegraphed swing. But before my arm can hit its target, he reaches out with both his hands. He holds the back of my head with his left and cups my mouth and nose with his right.

White fungus riddled nails, cut and scabbed digits - except the right ring finger that was missing - wrap around my mouth and nose. I figure his hands would smell like they looked: terrible. He has control of me. My old football coach always said: control the head, control the body. He has me by the head! He is now in control. I start to struggle, but cannot pull from the vice-grip he has on my face and head. I can't take a breath. Is he trying to suffocate me? His; warm and friendly expression doesn't change as I struggle to free myself by hitting him. I begin flailing at his midsection, Joe Frasier style, well at least I think he may have done it like this. Between body shots, he cocks my head so I am looking directly into his eyes. He says one word;

"Breathe."

Breathe? I can't breathe. I don't want to take a breath through that hand. He repeats:

"Breathe."

I feel his grip on my mouth and nose relax enough so I can free my mouth some. I yank my head back, struggling to get my mouth open enough to suck in a big breath. I am getting mouth claustrophobia, but before I can get a free and clear airway, I feel like I am about pass out so I have to suck in before I can clear his hand. I gasp, hell I was struggling for air.

Initially I believe I have lost consciousness and passed out before I can catch my breath. I am drifting away. I have to suck through his hand. Fuck! I force myself to draw a breath through his fingers, then another. My wits are returning, or are they? He won't release me. He clenches hard enough to require me to breathe through his hand, again I expect the smell of feces. Instead I start getting lightheaded. I close my eyes and inhale again. Oddly, the aroma is surprisingly engaging: pure clean bliss – breathtaking, in fact. What is happening? What the fuck?

My next breath is addicting. I crave breathing through his hand. With the second breath my stress, pain, hate, and frustration wash away. I gulp another. I grow euphoric. The smell is pure romance: lilacs, tangerines, floating on an ocean breeze. I keep swallowing gulp after gulp. Joy, happiness, laughter fill my heart, my chest. The aroma is magic.

Oh my God, oh my fucking God, it dawns on me, I know this smell. It is the scent of a woman, but not just any woman, it is hers. Yes! Oh my FUCKING GOD! It is my wife. And it wasn't just her aroma, but the essence of her. I could feel her. I could taste her. I could hold her. I can feel big bountiful, healthy, cancer-free breath, my hand on her warm chest. I can hear her laugh. She is with me now, there, in my head, my heart, my soul. But not just in my head like a great memory, it surrounds me mentally and physically real. It is as if I teleported to her. I grab his hand and suck in, hard, like a drowning man finally reaching the scuba air tank. Memories became more vivid, more colorful. Her voice - a healthy, happy voice I thought I would never hear again - rings through my ears.

"Baby it's me!"

We embrace. Tears again pour from my eyes, but this time they are tears of joy. I scream in ecstasy; outwardly crying. Looking up I see his face; unchanged, a face of pure contentment and satisfaction. I squeeze his hand harder, tighter and tighter onto my mouth. The feelings and experience amplified. AMPLIFIED! But how? I was flushed with great, vivid memories, not just memories: I was actually living these memories. I was speaking to her and she was answering me. She looks warm, healthy, and vibrant, the picture of health. I am on a different mental plane. Am I dreaming? And if I am dreaming I don't want it to stop. I must have died and am meeting her in heaven? He must have suffocated me to death. I don't give a fuck. I am with her.

No I'm not dead. I am staring right at him when I open my eyes. It gets even better. I feel bliss akin to the day I met her: happy, strong, and alive. I feel total joy and satisfaction. I feel healed. I have been made whole again. I have been made fucking WHOLE AGAIN! I feel the way I did when she walked next to me in public or when she lay sleeping nude next to me on a warm summer, Sunday morning.

We were dating for only a few months, studying at the university's library, holding hands. She squeezed my hand real 'tight' and told me she loved me for the first time. I wanted to tell her the first day I met, her but I didn't want to freak her out, scare her off, and I didn't have the nerve. And instead, she said it! SHE SAID IT! Leaving my feet I stretched across one of those big, mahogany study tables, draped myself over her, and couldn't let her go. I whispered in her ear:

"I fell in love with you the moment we met. I LOVE YOU!"

It was burnt macaroni every day at our first apartment. If we scraped together enough money Friday nights or took back empties, we'd buy a cheap bottle of wine. Never seemed to get through the mac and cheese, but we had wine and didn't care. We rush toward passion, harmonious rapture pulsing in perfect cadence, so *right* I worried about passing beyond ecstasy to exhaustion, salty wash of bodies entangled, separating just long enough to regain our breath. I thumbed the blond, baby soft hairs on the small of her back, glistening in the light cast by the street light outside. She rolls over with a satisfied - want more, addict's wildness in her eyes. The night breeze, the chill, beading sweat in the soft, concave flesh between hip bones. And she was all mine. The thrill, oh, the thrill.

I think I am drifting in and out of levels of consciousness I never knew existed, never before perceived, nor even heard described. I am where I want to be. The smell of Thanksgiving dinner wafts through my senses. Her mom, a great cook, is thickening gravy while she sifts flour over the pan, never a lump, never too salty. From the den I hear Grandmother, Mom and her sister scream with joy, whisk falling into the shallow pool of gravy with a tinny, dull ting. Laughter and joy fountain out from the kitchen. Three generations of females rush to me: hugs and congratulations abound. They fawn over her engagement ring that has caught their attention at the stove before we have had the chance to tell them.

She beckons me to come out to the backyard, the annual ritual of illegal leaf burning. She loves the smell when they dried and were just right to burn, usually early November. You were not supposed to burn them in the city anymore, but this year, like years past, she scoops a handful, packs them into a coffee can and lights them on fire. We'd sit on the swing in the backyard, bundled, at the cusp of winter, in the darkness of the evening to hide the billowing smoke and she would tell me the same story of how she and her grandpa raked leaves and burnt them on his farm, how she loved the smell. Of course there was wine then, too, and there she was - mine.

There is something sexy about cute, skinny, bony, little bare feet hurriedly tip toeing on a cold wooden floor back to the bed with the Sunday paper - the big, fat one with all the coupons and advertisement slicks in it. I'd rifle through the sports first, the business, entertainment, then finally the hard news. She would be tousling her hair, ripping out coupons and photos of furniture or drapes. God, she looked sexy doing everything. I never remember her ever using a coupon to purchase one item, but collecting them was her thing. Hours later, when strewn paper covered the bed and floor as if we were sloppily prepping to paint the ceiling, we would wrestle among the covers and papers, make love, then fire fighter, leap from bed, the last one out knowing they had to pick up the papers. She never noticed I always let her win – or maybe she did.

Now we are together. Where are we? Where am I? What are we? Not dreaming or imagining. We are in each other's presence. She smiles casually, like she always did when walking into the front door any day of the week. I respond, and we embrace. I am not talking and neither is she, but we are communicating. I can feel her; feel her from the inside. I am thinking with her, she with me. We are sharing our minds, our souls, and our existence. We are one. We are translucent, no lines of flesh separating us, no need for words; our thoughts, our conversation an exchange of thoughts, without speaking. Our minds have melded together working, sharing, laughing, loving as one. I am without my body and she, without hers. Are we in a place - a dimension - beyond description.

I note that yes, we are sharing past memories as old friends who haven't seen each other would do to rekindle a friendship, but we are also sharing the moment, the present I am in now, this moment; there! Where? I don't know. This isn't some mind trick, wrenching my favorite memories from my brain, is it? No! We are creating new memories together. We are there, together in the now. I just can't figure out where it is. But the feeling is so rich, so fluid, so satisfying I don't care where we are. I never thought I would ever love again yet I'm loving her again. Until this moment I believed that was impossible. It is our love cubed. It is the light of our love, but pure and more intense than I could have remembered when she was alive. Rapture is a pale word for how I, we, feel now.

Oddly, I have no impulse to ask her if she is okay, or in a good place - like a person at a séance might want to ask a dead relative. I know what she is thinking, and she knows that of me. She loves where she is. She loves the fact that I am now with her but also, and this is really strange, there is no feeling of missing each other, no fear of me leaving her, and no fear of the future, the past or the present moment. Whatever life concerns consumed me are distant. We are nestled in each other's soul, I think, bathed in true contentment, and requiring nothing. We have become one. Stripped of all earthy and physical being, I care not to understand my present existence. The boundaries of our souls no longer exist. We are one. She and I are now we.

My mind, and I think my body, have flashed from this empty office to this place I find that I now crave. The more I focus and breathe, the more I can stay with her. I never want it to end. I roll from my knees to a comfortable fetal position on the floor. He obliges me by squatting like a baseball catcher so his hand will not detach from my mouth. I keep breathing in - and for the first time in over a year I remember what life, love is supposed to feel like again.

10

Usually that's the second question asked,
number one is: Is there a heaven?

I don't remember passing out or falling asleep in that
empty office space but I suddenly found myself conscious,
awakening with a Christmas morning ease, perfectly fulfilled,
content and without hate or pain in my heart. I am on the floor in
front of the dented drywall. My "friend" is no longer there. It is
dark. I raise myself to a sitting position, trying to gather what is
left of my faculties to assess what has happened. Depression and
disappointment start to poison my newfound euphoria. My head
begins to ache. I am thirsty and alone.

"No you're not, I'm still here."

His voice pierces the silence and echoes off the walls of
the empty room. Sitting on the floor, I hurriedly spin myself
around on the axis of my left ass cheek. There he is sitting against
the opposite wall of the large space eating what looks like a rotten
banana. It looks like shit. It is so black.

"We can go get some good food if you'd like."

"No, this is enough."

It is almost too difficult to watch him eat it. But whoever this person or god is, he has what I want - at least I think he does.

"Could you please tell me what you did to me?"

"So we're going to talk?"

How could I not? The last - what? three hours? have been the best three hours of my life since she died.

"I did nothing to you that you can't do for yourself. I am just better at it right now."

He struggles to peel the bottom half of the black banana with his right hand, the one missing his fourth finger. I have to find out how he brought my wife back to me, or did he take me to her? I need to find out. I become anxious. I find myself concerned that he might just get up and walk away, never to be seen again, never helping me understand what has just happened. I wouldn't really blame him after what I did and said to him. I need to engage him, keep him present.

"What happened to your finger?"

"Someone bit it off."

He sees me wince.

"I am sorry ... bit it off?"

He cups his right hand over his mouth. The space where his missing ring finger would have been creases his lips. He starts breathing in and out, hard, then points to me with his left hand, smiles a wide grin, and chops down on his teeth to demonstrate. I guess I'm not the first person he has done this to. Someone else didn't want to lose their clench on his hand.

"Everything in my being, my commonsense, tells me that you are not God, and what I am is certifiably crazy."

"Well, you are not crazy, at least regarding me. You are just broken. But I started making you better. I have the time to talk if you do."

This is hitting an all-time high on my weird-shit-o-meter. I can't say I believe, but after what has just happened, I have to tell you, that was no magic trick. And if I can get that same feeling back someday, I am curious and serious enough that I will talk to God. I will talk to fucking anybody. A slight smile breaks through his carefree look.

"Okay, say I do believe, and you are what, God? And I am not nuts: Can we do this some other time? I have to get back to work and explain to them where I've been."

"Don't worry about them. They are all gone now."

"You didn't vaporize them or something?"

He laughs.

"No, it's after five o'clock: quittin time, and you know people on a Friday. They like to get out of the office as soon as they can."

He points to his wrist but there is no watch. If there was a way I could feel more like a dumb ass, insulting my gift horse by making the "vaporized" comment does the trick. I really want to walk slowly into this. I still have not dismissed the possibility that I am completely bonkers and will wake up in a loony bin when they adjust my meds, and the last six months have proven to be a medicated fog to deaden the pain. If this is a joke I'll bail, but what about her? I don't know what it was, and I don't know how he did it, but he gave me her - and I want her back.

"Okay, how does this work? Do I have to go to a church or climb to the top of a mountain and talk to a cloud or a bush? Do I have to build an arc?"

The smirk breaks into a wide grin.

"Arc, Bible humor, funny: Nothing fancy: You ask me questions, and I answer them. I will tell you this: It will be a lot to handle or process, so if you want to go in some order you can, or just fire away. I promise you that when we are done you WILL feel much better."

"You see, there are answers to questions that will clarify other questions, so if I think you can understand something better by giving the information to you in particular order, I will stop you and tell you we should talk about that in a bit. Regardless of how you choose to ask me questions, we will get through it. And you will feel a whole lot better."

I feel 10,000 times better already since that brief time I got to spend with my wife. I can't get the last few hours out of my mind. I have never taken drugs or had much to drink except for wine, so I can't even compare the feeling to anything even remotely that powerful. The memories and experience were more real than anything I have ever felt before, at least since she died.

He finishes his banana and rocks back against the wall, both of us now sitting on the floor. His left leg is straight out and his right is bent at the knee with his right hand propped atop it. He rolls his neck to crack it and shakes his shoulders, like a boxer before a fight. I stay about 10 feet in front of him, more to the center of the room. I take my keys from my pocket and sit Indian style. Can I say Indian style? Fuck it. I sit crossed legged in a yoga position. He settles in, smiles and arches his eyebrows, raising his chin to welcome the first question without speaking. I begin.

"If you are God-."

He quickly interrupts me.

"If you're going to start out each question with 'if you are God,' one, it will take too long, and two, it's a bit insulting, not to mention condescending."

"Sorry."

"How about this: For the sake of this conversation, you assume I am God until you think I am full of shit, and then you can leave or stay because you find me entertaining. I'm sure if I'm not, you're bright, you'll figure me a fool. Besides, I'm not much on

70

names. The name 'God' does not follow me around. It is the name you all made up to describe me here on earth."

"What do you mean, 'follow you around'? So there is other life in the universe besides our own?"

"Usually that's the second question asked. Number one is: Is there a heaven?"

"Well, is there?"

"I promise you that we won't leave until you get those answers, but let's start a little slower and ratchet up to the big questions. I'd hate to blow your mind this early in our journey. The times I have tried speaking to people here on earth in the past, I'm usually met with rudeness, hostility, doubt - even hate."

"Fair enough."

        A harvest moon offers shadowy lighting. I grab my cell phone from my pocket. I rarely use it for speaking now. My circle of friends closed when my wife passed away. She was our social life. I was the wheel man. I use it more now as a timepiece since I never got used to wearing a watch. I power it down and set it next to my keys. I feel some angst or trepidation as my mind swirled, thinking of my first question for God. For God? Fuck! This is fucking weird. What do I ask? Got it:

"When I was assaulting you in my madness, you said, 'God nor anyone else took my wife. God didn't have a plan for her. Your wife's body could no longer sustain her; she had to move on. What did you mean when you said that?"

"What part?"

"Can we take them in order?"

"Sure."

"Okay, you said first, 'God nor anyone else took my wife. What did you mean?"

"I don't take anyone. I don't look down from a cloud and say, 'Ah look at Joe the bricklayer. Heaven needs a good brick layer.' Then I strike him with a bolt of lightning, he dies, and comes to heaven because I said so. That is so not what I do. We are not set up that way. If you were to ask me my opinion, I would prefer that everyone live a long healthy life. The only actual plan for your time spent on earth is not derived from me but is predicated on your genetic makeup, how you take care of yourself mentally and physically, and a bit of luck. I'm not in the business of taking people. I never judge anyone. It goes against everything that is right, namely a human's ability to choose, to determine his or her own future, to control his own destiny."

"You're talking about free will?"

"Free will? Yeah, that's a good way to describe it: free will. You can't have 'free will'-"

He does the quotes in midair with the hand missing the finger-

" and have some supreme being hanging over you deciding what is right or wrong."

"Really? Everything I was told is that you are in charge. There is a master plan, and you decide who goes and when, and if I sin I can ask you for forgiveness."

"Nope, you got bad information. Probably from a religion."

"What did you mean when you said God didn't have a plan for her?"

"I don't plan people's lives. I don't have a plan for everyone. In truth, I don't have a plan, a destiny for anyone, like some religions persist on insisting. There are almost seven billion people on this planet - and more in other places."

"What? Did you say other planets?"

"We'll get to that later. Let's stay with the question. So, there are seven billion people on the planet. That's seven billion plans! Charting everyone's destiny and how they impact the destiny of everyone else flies in the face of free will. If it were true that I had a plan for everyone, the world would be a quiet, boring place. If people truly believed or became aware that they had no control over their destiny, and we are simple pawns in my chess game of life, they would just wait to see how I acted out my whims. They would become

lethargic and uninterested in growing, loving, trying new things, or living life with vigor or zest. Worse, they would act poorly."

"What do you mean act poorly?"

"If you knew, for the sake of this conversation, that there was a supreme being controlling your life, the human spirit which is in all of you, would lash out, trying to upset the master plan. Your human desire to achieve, love, grow, strive for goals, express your individuality - would be channeled to stopping the flow of my supposed super plan: my perfect vision of the world. You would look around and say, 'This is what the master wants, but it is not what I want' even if it's the perfect environment."

"Like the Garden of Eden?"

"Can we do bible stories in a bit?"

I nodded as to not slow his pace.

"As I was saying, even in a perfect world you will change a forced-upon-you existence any way you can. Everything that God finds to be right, you would find to be wrong. You would grow hostile toward me. You are built to desire free will and to choose your own destiny. It's not about right or wrong; it's about the celebrations of life, your free will. The human spirit must constantly be fed. It is what makes you survive. Check your history. Check out how humans have acted when they have faced a life without choice, without freedom, without free will."

"You mean the history of the world, here, when tyrants ruled countries with an iron fist? The human spirit of the people living under that oppression caused them to do everything to fight for a change, even die for it."

"For death will set them free. The greatest non-gift I can give the human race is to give you the ability to be your own person, make your own decisions, chart your own path, and be your own self-governing god. The human spirit requires free will. There is a natural compass, impulses, desires in all humans to survive, multiply, and know how to treat each other. That compass simply put is 'love.'"

"Love?"

11

Hold on! I like the God has a plan thing.
Not true, but I like it.

"Remember this and share this with anyone you choose: love cannot exist and flourish without freedom to choose - free will as you say - and without free will the human spirit will eventually die. Humans need free will to be able to love."

"Every person I spoke to as my wife was dying and after she died kept telling me that God has a plan for her. So I get it. No plan-"

He quickly cuts me off.

"Hold on! I like the God has a plan thing. Not true but I like it."

"Why?"

"Most religious leaders - priests, ministers, rabbis, pick your favorite religion - will say to survivors of a loved one who passes it's God's will or God has a plan for them, or they were needed in heaven. That is not true; if they knew about heaven they wouldn't say that. But if it helps people on earth to mourn a loved one who has evolved either because of old age or unexpectedly taken as in a car accident -"

"Or cancer?"

74

"Or cancer, it may ease the family's pain and help in their mourning process knowing that death was not a wasteful death or random bad luck, but a call from God - as if this person were important to my master plan, someone I needed to assist me in running this universe. It's not true, but I dig the fact that if people suffer less by me taking the blame or them thinking this was an act of God, I'm all for it. They don't realize the separation is only for a short period of time."

"Do you expect me to leave that 'separated for a short period of time' reference just floating out there without asking you what that means? I just lost my wife!"

"I was hoping it would slide by until we got to know each other more. You are not ready for that discussion yet. I tend to forget what evolutionary level on which I am presently speaking. Not just you, the entire species."

His eyes close for a moment. He takes a deep breath, his face enveloped in a painful grimace, holding his left side - I assume cracked ribs from my beating. Pondering, he rubs his crotch, then his brow, swings his weight from one ass cheek to the other, rocks down on his elbow apparently to get some relief from his ribs. Then he opens his eyes and smiles.

"Let me take a crack at this now, and then more later. Fair?"

"Fair."

"When the human species eventually evolves to its peak, there will be no separation when a loved one, as you say, dies. Because you are such a simple species, for now you cannot perceive what your eventual evolution and your abilities will truly be in a few years."

"Come on. Now *that* sounds like bullshit."

"Not at all. You will all be together as you go from one evolutionary level to another. You will be comfortable with the evolution when your intellectual ability as humans peaks."

"To clarify: When you say 'evolving' you mean dying."

75

Talk to God

"Well actually to truly clarify, when you say dying you as a human, today, believe that the deceased ceases to exist. Maybe you imagine them or their souls in heaven, but all you know for sure right now is that you stop communicating with them."

"That's not true?"

"Do you really think you are presently at your intellectual peak? You're not even close. Your egos are ahead of the curve, but your brains are infantile compared to the final evolution. When you do you will have the ability to communicate and -"

"My eighth grade teacher used to say we only use about ten percent of our brains. I guess he was correct?"

"He's going in the right direction. At least he got the perception that you haven't even come close to the full use of your brain. If he would have said that we are only using one-thousandth of our brains, he would be closer to being correct than saying ten percent. But remember, he, too, is only using a tiny portion of his brain, albeit more than most. We have a long way to go before you get it."

"Great, so we are presently too stupid to get it, that there is a life after death? But if you told me and I shared it with the world, wouldn't it make people who are losing someone, like me, more comforted when their loved one dies?"

"To understand and appreciate the evolution of the human soul - or as you call it 'the spirit' on its journey to the next level, you are going to have to advance that melon of yours a few more million years. Now, I am not trying to avoid answering the question: I will. But I will do everything I can to put it into terms you can process. Know this though: If I were to explain it to you straight without dumbing down the framing of the information to your present intellectual state, it would be like you trying to explain to your dog how to assemble a laptop computer from scratch. There are no words in the human language yet to describe the evolution, but if you have the patience, I will explain it to you as simple as I can."

"Come on, what could be so hard? You're speaking English."

"You still don't get the problem."

He leans in, making sure that I attend to his point.

76

"Imagine that American settlers living in the early 1800s time travel to today and are listening to two auto mechanics from the local car dealership discussing a car's air conditioning system. They don't know what a car is, much less air conditioning or Freon. It would sound like gibberish to them."

"So I get it. The present human species wouldn't understand it even if you spoke it to me in plain English."

"Yep."

"You said you would help me understand though."

"I really don't want to get stuck on this point. How about I give you an example of what amazing things the human mind will have the ability to do once developed, and then you will see how death or the evolution to a new level will be a seamless transition with no separation? Then we'll move on. Promise?"

"Promise"

"Did you like being with your wife again?"

I shudder, my eyes welling with tears. I cannot speak. My throat tightens. The reality of my human existence just did an about-face and slammed me right back in the mouth. He knows he is doing it and he knows I would react like that. I almost forgot how much I miss her. The time with her, a junkie's fix: I crave more. I put my head in my hands. I am scared this is a sick joke or cosmic parlor trick. I nod.

"Yes! I fucking liked being with my wife! Please do not fuck with me on that subject."

"Fear not. She will always be available to you. And in a few million years you - or I should say, your mind - will have the ability and more importantly, the capacity, to share and grow with her on the human plane, while she is transitioning and, to keep this simple, on 'other' planes after someone dies."

"Are you saying …"

"I thought we were going to move on?"

77

"Hold the hell on! Are you saying that humans cannot have that gift until we evolve in a few million years?"

"Not at all and it is not a gift it is an eventual human ability. All who move on, evolve, or as you say, die, will be able to enjoy the same experience that you enjoyed with your wife a few hours ago. Evolved humans and those who are left behind on earth, like you and your wife, in a few million years from now will communicate as their loved ones evolve and become part of their new existence. I just gave you a preview."

I find myself riveted to his explanation. I get it. I think. I am fascinated by his comfortable pace and the measured tempo of his answers. You immediately get the impression that this is not the first time he has described his perceptions.

My left leg keeps falling asleep while I'm sitting on the floor. I stand to shake my pants and boxers down out of my ass crack. A chill shivers down my spine. The sweat from our tussling, now dried to a tacky, matted hair, need-a-shower glaze on my forearms, requires a brisk rub.

"Are you cold?"

"It's been a long day."

I grab my cell phone on the floor to check the time: ten past eight.

"Do you want to stop?"

"Nope."

I stand and tentatively begin walking toward the wall he is leaning against. I motion with my hand, inviting myself to sit next to him, seeking approval, to share the wall he is leaning on. He carelessly nods his approval. He doesn't care if I sit against the wall, stand on my head, or plop on his lap. What the fuck do you ask someone who tells you he is God and proved to me he is not ordinary. I want to see if I can test him so I press:

"The third phrase you said was that my wife's body could no longer sustain her, she had to move on. I am an educated man, so when I hear you say, 'no longer sustain her,' I assume you mean her body was wracked with cancer, and so she was dying, but what *do* you mean by 'she had to move on'?"

"I will give you the simple answer. And then I will ask that you not ask me the next question that pops into your head because it will require one of those answers that will be better explained if you are aware of everything in order. So I am going to answer your question now, but please allow me the time to give you an extended explanation a bit later so you may understand better. Deal?"

Do I have a choice? I nod my head in agreement.

"Your wife is not dead. She evolved, actually to a more advanced existence as, you will, too, someday, and she's now part of the ever-expanding universe. In fact, her existence along with everyone else's existence fuels the growth of the universe. The human soul, your spirit, is much more advanced than you could imagine. You are extremely important in the expansion of the universe."

"There are only so many pieces to this puzzle called the universe, and not one is ever wasted or slips away to nothing. It is impossible for anything in the universe to just disappear. Energy, matter, continues to flourish, to grow, to expand – it never disappears. You are all on a long journey, far beyond this simple existence on this planet. You have barely scraped the surface of your evolution. Using your earthly description, 'her soul' is fine; intact and full of more life than ever before. Remember when I said that humans actually only use one-thousandth of the brain's capacity? It's even more complicated. In addition to growing your brain a thousand times over generations there are 100 steps in becoming the being I, me, the universe has created. Presently an adult human is maybe at the third or fourth step in your development. You are virtually fetus-like compared to your final and fully matured species."

"So you mean-?"

He quickly cut me off.

"I said: no additional questions on this topic now. Appreciate what you have just learned. Let's move on."

"Please, one question!"

He likes my new-found enthusiasm for our conversation, I can tell. He rolls his eyes, shakes his head. He's giving into me, the child. He smirks.

"Okay, one question. Fire."

"Why don't you tell everybody this?"

"You mean tell all humans that when they die here on earth the journey continues?"

"Yes, wouldn't it be a better place?"

"Would it? First, for years I have been telling everyone I meet and oftentimes I show them, including you, that there is another step, and you know what? They don't believe a word I say. When religions started to form from the stories I am telling you, I thought they were a good idea here on earth since you were not very advanced."

He points to the side of his head.

"I thought they would be the public relations department, helping humans to understand how things were set up, where you go after death, and the fact that it is a much better place - an advanced evolution of your being. But religions have totally screwed that up. They were supposed to have a few simple messages I gave them over the years, the stuff I am now sharing with you. But most of them don't really believe because they don't understand, and they go from sharing a simple message of love to getting into the business of scaring people for money."

"Second, if people did know the actual evolution of their spirit, their souls, at their so called death, they would begin killing themselves to evolve to a higher level quicker because of the advanced quality of existence their death would take them to. Eventually the earth would be filled with simpleminded children, who have no knowledge of why they are going to kill themselves when they turn, say nine years old, but since everybody is jumping off the cliff at nine, why wouldn't a simpleminded nine year old not follow suit? At your present mental state you cannot cope with knowing so maybe it's best for the next step to be unknown and frightening."

"That is why it is extremely important for the human evolution to take place, for you to grow from a child into adulthood before you can move on. People with little or no

80

experience or love on earth have a more difficult time understanding and enjoying their evolution. I got to pee."

"What? Let me make sure I got all this straight."

"Oh, a recap. Recap then piss. Make it fast!"

God has to pee. Funny.

"One. . . "

He stands up and anxiously paces in his need to relieve himself. I hurry.

"You prefer that everyone live a long healthy life."

"Yes."

"… my time on earth is determined by my genetic makeup, how I take care of myself mentally and physically, and luck."

"You got it."

"There is no 'master plan' for me or anyone else. Free will also means free of a plan from God. "

"That's it. And?"

"And what?"

"And I got to piss! Hurry up!"

"Three, my wife's body gave out so she moved on to a higher evolutionary plane - a place that you took me to, right? Am I right?"

"Yes; kind of. Are we through?"

"You mean through through or just through until you're done peeing?"

"Yes, time to pee."

He stands up and brushes himself off. Plumes of white drywall dust roll off his shoulders, elbows, and forearms. He rolls and cracks his neck, shoots me a quick, satisfied smile and walks out the door to, I assume, the men's room in the hall. The only two words I can think of to describe my present state of mind are lunacy and euphoria.

12

Can you have lost your mind and still evaluate
your present mental stability to determine
if you lost your mind. What the fuck am I talking about?

If you are capable of thinking that you may have lost your mind, have you truly lost your mind? Or are you just touched but not totally incurable? Can you have lost your mind and still evaluate your present mental stability to determining if you lost your mind? What the fuck am I talking about?

I keep trying to process the last few hours. Being emotionally and physically exhausted does not afford me the ability to think clearly. I don't really care if I have lost my mind, or whether this guy is God or the television repairman. What I do know is, for what seemed like days, he took me back to my baby. He made me whole again, even if it was just for a short time. He gave me the chance to hold her, to kiss her, to love her again and I want her back right now, my four-fingered friend is the ticket.

A hard floor, and I in my 40's, do not make for much comfort. I lay flat and stretch, my arms above my head reaching as high as my body will allow. It feels good to unwind. I point my toes and tighten my leg muscles nearly to cramping. I relax and bring my hands to my sides, coiling slowly into a sitting position. I

83

lean forward and can almost touch my toes. Bobbing back and forth, my lower back slowly begins to loosen and I am able to just barely reach my shoes. And yes, for the first time since her death, there is an "at ease" pace to my being. It feels good: the feeling you get when everything is right in the world. It's been a while.

I lay there smirking, staring at the cheap lowered ceiling panels stained from a water leak, thinking back to what hurt most about my wife dying. It wasn't my selfish perspective of living in a loveless void, or losing my best friend, my soul mate. It was the knowledge that she was alone, frightened and in great pain on her final journey and I was powerless to help her or do anything about it. You see, death is a journey you take alone. Support, hospice, husbands, priests, and prayers are for the survivors. Cancer death slow dances alone with your mind. There is no support group for the internal torture and strife. Cancer doesn't kill you, fear does. It hollows your brain into submission and I could do little to help her.

The one thing that I did bring to our very lopsided relationship was that I took care of her, the little things. I held the umbrella, rubbed her arms until the goose pimples disappeared, went for the aspirin, warmed up the car, got the coats, rubbed her feet, swatted the bugs, and wiped up the yucky things. All the little bumps in life were never her problem. I protected her from bad waiters and the endless line of guys hitting on her. The drunks were the worst, but I got good at defending her honor, protecting her dignity without getting knocked on my ass. As good as I got at it, I couldn't help her those last six months of her life. The guilt was killing me up until three hours ago. The anvil of guilt pressing down on my chest has disappeared.

Now I know that she is not alone, not in pain; in fact she has evolved to a higher plane, a wonderful place, someday "our place." Knowing that I will see her again, be with her again and love with her again, has given me great joy and has cleansed me of my guilt. I will sleep well tonight hoping to meet her in my dreams. Life as I know it has already changed forever - again.

I want to see her again. Dare I ask him? For the last three months I have done everything possible to forget her.

Everything. All I want to do now is be with her, and I know now she is not gone. The urge is palpable. That schoolboy, first love, twist in my gut is back. Oh, how can this be real? Is it real? Am I dreaming, delusional, mad?

Fifteen minutes is a long time to take a leak, even for God. What if he has left? Disappeared, to find another broken soul to fix? I get nervous; scared that I will lose her, uh him, again! I get to my feet and run to the restroom, pulse racing in fear that I am truly mental chum, and I have been talking to a plant or filing cabinet all evening or that he is gone and with him goes my beloved.

I burst into the men's room: cheap fluorescent bulbs, half of which work, flicker on as I pass the motion sensor. I find my God sleeping in a dried pool of piss under a wall urinal. His left shoe, the woman's gym shoe, has slipped off his foot. The foot is covered in pus, blisters, dirt and angry - looking calluses. He has installed a dried pig ear given to dogs to chew as a replacement for the sole of the shoe which has a worn hole. Disgusting would not come near to describing his feet.

He sleeps easily, a satisfied expression riding the bellows of his open-mouth breathing. I go to the sink and turn on the water, finding a warm, then closer to hot, water temperature. I gather what remained of the industrial brown hand towels from the dispenser. Wetting half with warm water, I kneel in front of him and begin washing the vile residue from a foot that has not been washed in eons. The warm water amplifies the pungent aroma. By the second pass, he is startled awake.

"Why are you doing that?"

"Your feet looked infected. I thought I could return the kindness for …?"

I stammer, hesitate. I cannot say what I am thinking.

"for … for … for…."

"… for being with your wife again, right?"

85

"Yes! I am so sorry. I don't know how to describe it. It seems beyond real, hard to comprehend."

"Yeah, it is a bit of a shock to most people. I am glad you dug it."

He looks down at his shoe and foot, embarrassment on his face.

"I appreciate the gesture. How about doing the right one and skipping the left? There is dried blood or something that holds the left one in place, and I don't want to chance losing the seal and the boot since I don't have a lace for it."

"What happened to the lace?"

"I gave it to a guy who needed it more than I did."

I have got to stop asking these questions because the answers are always "the-right-thing-to-do" kind of answers; 'All The Right Stuff' movie kind of shit. Nothing makes sense. He speaks like a Rhodes Scholar but lives on the street. And for lack of a better universally accepted name, he goes by - no, he is God.

"Can we continue to talk?"

"Yeah, that's why I came. We can talk as long as you want. But let's walk and talk. It will be dawn in awhile, and I am sure they won't want us loitering around this building on a Saturday."

"We can go to my place?"

"You are not ready to go home now. There is plenty more work to do before we go home. Why don't we walk for coffee? Doesn't that sound good?"

It does. Especially as I pry a wedge of what looked like manure, blood, and silt from between his toes. He never misses a beat as he speaks. I don't know what he means by the fact that there is plenty of work to do before I can go home, but everything about this experience still reeks of the macabre so I am rolling with it.

"Can I see my wife again?"

I thought I would just hit him with it. I am craving it. He smiles widely.

"I am sure we can figure out something. Let's see how the next few hours go. You know, when you eventually evolve, you won't need my tricks to be with people after they have also evolved."

I finish washing his foot. I dry it with the remaining paper towels. I slide the pig ear back in the shoe, covering the worn hole, and then slip the shoe over his foot. We help each other up and begin walking out of the building.

Walking shoulder to shoulder, we approach the mirrored glass lobby. Fear grips me, again concerned that when we pass the mirror I will see only myself, walking alone, talking to myself, a bumbling fool. Nope, he is there. I feel so much better when I see him. Not that loony after all.

We walk out into the cool, early morning air. The chill feels good, my face tightens and my nose begins to run a bit. The world has yet to wake. No cars, street noise, dogs barking, just an eerie void of all noise, and I feel safer and more comfortable then than I ever have. We decide to head toward the closest Starbucks, 15 minutes by car, but we are hoofing it. The freshly clean right foot, with the pig ear in the gym shoe, seems to not have settled comfortably and he keeps stopping to adjust the pig ear.

"Would you like some help?"

"Nope, I am good. What is on your mind?"

13

Do you listen to my prayers, to everyone's prayers?

We walk in silence for probably a half of a mile. There is a recklessness about the moment. I have the guy with me that could answer all the questions that have consumed man since the beginning of time, and he's walking next to me, with a pig ear in his shoe. His lack of God-like powers and his lack of any resemblance to any image of any deity I'd ever read about or heard of tests my credulity at every turn. He can tell I was becoming uneasy, vexed.

"Just relax. Start with something not so profound or immense. Ramp it up a bit."

"You mean like why is the ocean blue?"

"It not. Neither is the sky."

"What?"

"Come on, you knew that. The sky isn't blue and the sun isn't yellow but white. It just looks that way to your eye. The ocean absorbs colors in the red part of the spectrum and leaves behind the blue colors. And there you have it, whammo blue ocean."

"Really?"

"Yeah, but you didn't need me for that one. I saw it on the Discovery Channel when I was walking the mall, warming up, a few weeks back. Nice start though."

"I'm just getting warmed up."

If he really wants me to challenge him I'll challenge him. I can tell he is dying to get peppered with question, almost like a chance to show off. I should have attended religious studies more often as a child.

"Do you listen my prayers, to everyone's prayers?"

"I never listen. Unless you start praying while I am standing next to you, I can't hear a thing. So it is not like I can hear all the prayers and choose not to listen or to grant wishes; I don't listen because I can't hear them. So if you pray before bed or in church, save your breath. I do not hear them. And to make matters worse for the person praying, I really can't answer them. Prayers do work, though."

"Really? How's that, if God can't hear them?"

"Earlier I mentioned to you that the human soul, your spirit and your mind, is still infantile compared to your eventual capability. Your minds, your souls, your spirits are extremely powerful - as you will learn someday. When you are happy or sad people around you feel it. They can feel your emotions and you can feel theirs. You refer to this at church as praying. You refer to this feeling between one another as love. You will someday communicate with one another, with your spirit, your soul, and your mind."

"I don't get it."

"When totally developed, your minds will soon be your primary and most powerful communicators. Today you see someone who is very happy because you see them smile or perhaps even laugh. Actually, you are also feeling their positive, happy energy. I have heard it referenced in this era as 'putting out a vibe.' It is the first baby steps of your future existence beyond this earth. The 'vibe' you are putting out impacts everyone and usually requires a response from people around you. You have heard people say that 'so-and-so's laughter is contagious,' or that 'when so-and-so enters a room everyone notices.' Every human has this ability to use their mind to share with others their thoughts, their wishes, and yes their prayers. This will someday become the preferred way to

communicate. Remember, today you only are using one thousandth of your minds. You are callow in your present ability."

"So how does that affect someone saying a prayer?"

"They are communicating- not with me, God - but to all the people around them. They are emoting a message: a feeling of need, desire, happiness, or sorrow, and everyone around them is picking up on it. Now here's where it gets like me trying to describe to your dog how a laptop computer works. So if you don't get it, stop me and we'll try again. The power of a person's spirit who responds to another person's wishes-"

I interrupt him.

"A prayer?"

"No it doesn't have to be a prayer. It could be someone just concentrating extremely hard, wishing or hoping that will create 'the vibe' if they are so moved. And that vibe, as you will learn, becomes extremely powerful beyond earth. That vibe drives the universe. But don't confuse this. Forget about prayers. You don't need to pray to communicate with others. That's a religious definition, not a human or God thing. When you are concentrating on your wishes, focusing on something you desire or wish to share, your soul and spirit are reaching out to all other humans near you, using your brain as the communicator and returning the support to you. If the people near you are aware and are moved to respond, they will. And that response is a powerful, electric, spirited response that carries with it the ability to give that person the supporting power, the strength and ability to assist them in doing whatever it is they desire. And what all humans desire, and the energy that is exchanged with one another, in human terms, is love."

"So church services are a waste of time?"

"That's what you got out of all that? On the contrary: Churches amass large groups of people, and they focus on one common theme. Some have you join hands or sing but they are all, typically, on the same page and that is usually sharing of love. When someone says that their experience in church was moving and they think I had something to do with it, they are wrong. What made everyone in that church feel better was not God, but the power of the people sitting next to them. It was the energy you exchanged with each other. So I like churches because they bring people together to celebrate, share, and grow together through the energy of each other. Any time a group of people assemble for a common cause, amazing things can happen."

"You mean like people all praying at the Wailing Wall or at The Vatican?"

"Yes, but you are still focused on religion or a place to get these feelings or to get closer to me. It doesn't matter what the location. Actually sporting events and especially music concerts are better conductors and more enriching for the soul than church. The church is based on false prophets and old stories passed down through the generations, and most are wrong. Fact is, most people sitting in church believe only 30 percent of what they hear. Music concerts, no matter the kind of music, take the human soul to its present highest evolution. All attending are focused on a common goal, and the power in that environment is thick and palpable. It's the closest humans have come so far to how I thought people should be: celebrating life and love together in a large group."

"So you're a concert fan?"

"I love all music and some performers are truly disciples of the message of love and the energy in the universe."

"Who do you like?"

"My favorite in this generation is Dave Mathews and his band. He had horrible luck with his family. Parents dying, sister killed by her husband who then killed himself and he takes care of her children. You could relate to this. One of his band members just evolved after a car accident and a prolonged fight to survive. And through it all, the love in his heart prevailed and most all his songs are about true love. Other people would have been crushed by what he went through, but he draws the strength from his family and thousands of loving fans every night and gives it back to them. He is truly a disciple of God spreading and sharing the message of love."

"What's your favorite?"

"Favorite what?"

"Song."

God blushes as his fanaticism for Dave Matthews Band begins to show.

"Everyday. It is this generations anthem to what all humans need; love. Listen to the words someday. You'll think he wrote it about you and your wife. It speaks exactly how I thought you all should be to each other. The guy sings right from his heart: incredible. It

91

is how two people should be when they are being. This guy truly gets it. If I had disciples, he would be one of them. He creates the message of love and then shares it with millions of people each year. He's the goods. I have many favorites but DMB and the "What's Going On" album by Marvin Gaye are my favorites."

"So music is important."

"Have you ever been to some sort of celebration where music was not present? It is the nectar of this God and what makes a human the most joyous. You've been to concerts, right? There are 20,000 people all pouring out their love and joy to one another as they listen to the music that they all love. The venues are full of energy. There is excitement. The lights go down, the music goes up. People rise to their feet. The singer begins, and everyone cheers. The evening becomes spiritual. Everyone there are on the same page: loving the same music and all at the same time sharing their love with each other for the moment. Their life's problems fall away, exposing the joyful soul that is in all of you. And when your spirits and your souls are freed of the stress and emotional turbulence you pile on yourselves every day, the true nature of the power of your soul and spirit can expand and take you to wonderful places."

"I always thought people would live in large groups like that because of the wonderful feeling you share and the strength you have together. You might say that these things - the power of a group when you are all together - can help another human in need. God doesn't listen to prayers or answer them; the people around you do."

"Hold on, I must have had 3,000 friends and family members praying for my wife. She died. So much for the power of the people. On top of that you give me some hippie, Woodstock bullshit?"

"Someone saying a prayer to 'God' for your wife at church or at their home does little to impact that person. There is no link to each other's souls and spirit. There probably was not a connection because they were not near her to support her with their actual being. They were not opening their hearts and soul's to your wife and your wife had no idea if that person was reaching out to her or how to accept that kind of support."

"Forget the idea that you say your prayers at night, that I listen, and that I then grant your wish. The power to change, to cure, to educate, and enlighten lies among each other. It is there so you all can enjoy it. You can impact change. It is a great gift that you just haven't figured out yet how to use it yet because you have not developed enough yet. And you don't have to wait for any god to allow you the power to use it. Your present

ignorance on this matter leads to your anger and rage regarding your wife, not just you, but everyone here on earth."

"Could my wife have been saved if we all focused on her cancer in her presence?"

"Possibly in a couple 100,000 years. You have not yet developed, so you can't actually use these capabilities. In a few thousand generations your wife would have felt she was ill the moment the cancer appeared. She would have alerted her circle of loved ones who would have then focused on beating it but not now you are not mentally ready."

"So much for the power of the people. What about –"

He interrupts me..

"I know this is not going to make you feel any better, but it is just the time of your development as humans when many more people die of cancer than generations before you and there's even more that will succumb in the generations that will follow you."

"Great. Why us? Why now?"

"Your science and medicine have extended the age during which you live on earth. I had figured women to live to 40 or 45 years and men 35 to 40 and then they would move on to the next evolution in the universe. What science and medicine did was extend the ages of humans to nearly double that. The bi - product of extending the spirit and the soul's existence in the human form is that your body was not 'designed' for life beyond that age."

"So I am supposed to be dead now, too?"

"I can't say, as I mentioned earlier it is based on genetics: how you take care of yourself physically and mentally and some luck. But let's look at a woman for a moment. The way I figured it, a woman would live to her mid-40s. She would evolve into adulthood in her early teens, have her children in her mid to late teens, and enjoy the next 25 years raising them. She is supposed to have her family at a younger, stronger age. What kills a woman now-"

"Cancer?"

"Cancer is just a human, natural process of evolving to the next level. In women it's the reproductive organs that are not supposed to perform into her late 40s and 50s. So if you look at where most of the areas of a woman's body are attacked by cancer -"

". . . her reproductive organs?"

"Yes. The body is discarding those parts that are no longer needed. Cancer, menopause, Alzheimer's, old age in general – these are new killers your generation is creating right now. If you wish to continue on lengthening your time on earth, you need to address these things you call diseases, or what I refer to as natural aging. You have found ways to extend age but not the cures for the biproducts that come with extending the age of a person."

14

*The cure for an individual's cancer
is inside each and every one of you.*

"Will we find a cure for cancer?"

"I don't know the future anymore than you do. But what I know of other places you will mentally grow enough to figure it out. I will offer you a tip for the cure for the 200 different cancers that exist today."

I stop walking and confront him.

"Excuse me. You can't bullshit me on this topic. It hurts too much. You know there is no cure for cancer here."

"Yeah, I know, and I wouldn't think of bullshitting you. Cancer is as much a part of the human body as older people's hair turning gray. People suggest that minimizing stress or having a good diet will stop cancer. Wrong. Cancer is locked and loaded into your DNA the moment you are conceived, just like the color of your eyes or the shape of your face or length of your feet. When a person passes a certain 'worn' age – "

"What do you mean a 'worn age'?"

"You like that? Your body ages based on your genetic makeup and how you take care of yourself. Rarely does a person's age reflect their true aging. When I was explaining it to

some children a while back, I referred to a person that may look older than his or her age as a 'worn age.' This is the age your body feels not the years old you may be. Does that make sense to you?"

"Yes. I guess."

"So when a person reaches a certain age their body begins to evolve to the next level. This comes in the way of wrinkled skin, losing hair - you know: getting old. One of the aging elements that occurs very late in life and remember I mean life expectancy as long as I originally figured 'late in life' to be..."

I interrupt him.

"Forty or fifty right?"

"Yep, one of the aging elements here on earth, that effect some people is what you call cancer. Humans use medicine to extend life much longer than I had anticipated. Now if you can cure cancer you can live a much longer life. So for the last 50 years you have been focused on trying to change natural aging and cure cancer. As you may or may not know, cancer is not a term describing a single disease."

"Yeah, I know. I got the crash course when my wife was fucking dying."

"Good, then this will be easier for you. Cancer is personal and affects anyone who gets it in their very own personal way. It is in your DNA, your genes, and is one of the natural trigger for moving you on to the next evolution or plain. It is a unique disease for each person who gets it. Generally speaking a mutation will arise spontaneously without apparent cause. These mutations alter the DNAs molecular strands, not allowing cells to divide."

"So?"

"So? So that's cancer, and that is as far as your scientists have gotten. What they can't figure out is why the mutation occurs. And here is where it gets really crappy for you to try to figure this out. Even if and when you do someday get something to stop the cancer from growing, cancer like the power of your brain, is a very powerful part of your human biological makeup, and it will find a way around the cure you have created and the aging process (cancer) will simply begin again."

"The real reason for cancer being such a tough disease to cure is that the person who usually gets cancer is in their 40s or 50s and by my calculations, should have been dead already. The mutation or cancer is a bi-product of DNA that has passed its time. The body should have evolved. The soul and the spirit evolving to a higher evolution and the body, and its cancer would never be a concern because you should be dead already. You are attempting to cure something that was given to each human with the sole purpose of killing you so you will evolve. It's not a disease, it's is the solution to continue on to your destiny. "

"Hold on. Kids get cancer."

"Yes they do, and you can also lump in mental and physical handicaps into what I am about to say. Some people just get a bad genetic mix. It is not the fault of the parents. It is just a bad combination of genes. The genetic roulette wheel comes up double zeros. Whenever you deal with millions of people and billions of gene combinations you will always get a percentage of less than desirable combinations. But "it is just not handicapped or healthy; there is an entire genetic range we all deal with. It ranges from the severely mentally handicapped; to your Uncle Eddie whose left eye lid twitches when he chews his food. Perfection is rare. You all have some genetic flaws, some are just more noticeable than others; one extreme is kids get cancer."

"Well that all makes sense in the grand scheme of things, but right now we all here on planet 'stupid' would love to find a cure. You said you were going to give me a tip for finding a cure for cancer. What is it?"

" The tip? They need to stop looking for a cure for something that is part of the body's natural aging process. Cancer is part of you from the beginning. If you are treating a person with cancer you are too late to cure it. You are working on trying to kill an existing cancer cell. Once it's active you are screwed. You have to isolate the sequence of genetic information that creates the cancer flare-up, the mutation prior to discovery. Cancer is only beaten before it rears its ugly head. But they will not be able to cure it until they get their arms around DNA and how cancer is laced into your genetic makeup."

"The tip!"

"The cure for an individual's cancer is inside each and every one of you. You carry the cure within your bodies, in your DNA. You have some sharp guys getting close. Geneticists going into never "before" imagined directions in genomic medicine will eventually find 'your cure.' You have isolated a gene that does not allow the mutation to

begin. There are at least two required to stop cancers, and in some cases a combination of three to stop the growth of cancer cells."

"Sometime soon you will find the proper combination with those genes and a few others and will, I guess for lack of a better word, 'trick' your mind and body into feeling and believing you are younger, thus never beginning the actual process of mutation into cancer cells. You will cure cancer by actually finding the genetic process of slowing aging - the fountain of youth. In addition to stopping cancer from evolving, you will also slow aging in the process."

"To discover the medical fountain of youth would be awesome. People could live without cancer and live into their hundreds."

"You'd think. But in other civilizations that have developed to a higher mental level and have cured their cancer, who are well beyond your present stage, are you ready for this: they have stopped curing life-threatening cancers and diseases even though they have the knowledge, technology, and in most cases the cure to do so."

"Really?"

I have to tell you that I am amazed at my God. Here is a homeless guy who smells like urine, dresses in the dirtiest clothes, is missing a finger, and wearing a woman's sneaker, breaking down DNA and the cure for cancer for me. This can't get any weirder, can it?

"So why did they stop trying to cure life-threatening diseases on other planets?"

"Someone living in their human state had an advanced brain, a freakish occurrence but he had developed well ahead of everyone else. He started making contact with people who had evolved, like you did with your wife back at the empty office. The information about the next evolution being such an amazing existence for your soul and spirit made it back down to their planet. The only similar reference I could make here on Earth is your psychics. They have some advanced ability but nothing like this person. Your psychics have packaged what little they can do into a hustle to take advantage of people in pain."

"Not cool."

"Really not cool. Back to this person; initially inhabitants there thought this person to be a god. He became the conduit to all that had evolved. But after this person started

working with people who were about to die, telling them that he will contact them upon their evolution, and he did, that's when people's direction regarding healthcare changed on that planet. He shared with people how the superior existence they will enjoy after they evolve. And with the knowledge that after you pass you are aware of loved ones, and your existence was far more superior, the inhabitants of that planet began to not want to live long lives. They wanted to move on faster, so they stopped curing diseases and fell back to a natural order of their evolution because they believed it was what was their 'God' required. I didn't though. They just created the theory and ran with it just like you guys are doing here with your religions."

"Could you give me a comparison so I could appreciate my present existence on this planet as well as the new frontier my wife is enjoying and I will someday soon as well...?"

"... so being back with her and the way you felt didn't put a button on it for you?"

"... I'm still trying to get my head around it"

"Okay, a comparison of your present existence and hers. Sure, got it. A glass of water compared to the Pacific Ocean."

"What?"

"You asked for a comparison. If your existence on earth is measured as a glass of water, your next evolution, comparatively, would be the Pacific Ocean."

"Right."

"Just the response I would expect. It's just too much for you to handle right now. Remember you are presently incapable intellectually of processing it. If all were aware of the grandeur of the next level of existence you would all want to die in order to evolve. You are all too simple, too scared, to understand that the next step is a better existence and a step someday that will not require separation like you just went through. There are other places..."

"Other places?"

"We'll do spacemen in a bit. There are other places, civilizations in the galaxy, that have evolved, and they celebrate death, not as a sad time but an extremely happy time in their lives. Imagine having a celebration like a birthday party here for what you describe as a

terminal decease. This particular planet's inhabitants that received a terminal disease termed it 'the calling,' and it was celebrated. For the record I don't call anybody."

He reaches his hands to the stars, rolls his head back, angles his face skyward and screams.

"Free will for everybody!"

Then he pauses and takes a breath and smiles.

"Are you starting to feel better?"

I smile and nod my approval. I really wasn't sure.

"Let's move on."

There is comfort in the knowledge that I will again be with my true love.

15

There is an odd sensation of contentment
when you start believing the homeless person you are talking
to is truly God. Does that sound odd to anyone else?

There is an odd sensation of contentment when you start believing the homeless person you are talking to truly is God. Does that sound odd to anyone else? I don't know how far we have walked.

As the darkness gave way to Saturday morning's blue skies, I find myself purposely walking shoulder to shoulder with him sharing the same steady gate. Occasionally I allow my hand to touch his hand as they swing by each other. I am so curious as to 'what' he is? Man? God? Mortal? Alien? I make a veiled request to closely examine the stenciled name on his army jacket so I can touch him near his chest to see if he is breathing, has a pulse, heartbeat or is a Martian. And I think more importantly, I want to make sure that I didn't spend the evening with a figment of my imagination again. Could my new best friend truly be God, because God always rolls out with guys like, like … me? I am awash with amazement, disbelief, and contentment; odd emotional bedfellows.

I think my Army jacket examination ploy is working. I am fumbling with his jacket, flattening my open hand on his heart.

101

I try to deflect the clumsy moment by explaining that the horsehead shield on his shoulder is for the Army's 1st Cavalry division. I think I feel his heart beat.

"Does the Army still ride horses?"

I have no clue, at all. I once saw the patch on an old uniform of a Viet Nam vet interviewed on the History Channel. It was a piece on the upcoming Memorial Day weekend. As I am about ready to certify my true ignorance regarding the Army with an even more cockamamie backstory about the patch on his shoulder, he grabs my wrist.

"Hold on a minute!"

We stop. He motions me with his left hand to follow him into an alley we have just passed. What harm can there be, I am with God, right? The alley stinks of old fryer grease and wet exhaust. He finds the quietest spot afforded in any public alley: the crotch of a cinderblock wall and one of those industrial, metal dumpsters, the kind you would find my friend sleeping in or eating out of. Kicking a Styrofoam, take-out container, full of maggot infested Mexican food and what looks like human waste, he looks at home here. He spins and faces me.

"I thought we went through this last night? So you still don't believe I am human?"

I am startled. And busted.

"Actually I'm still worried that you are not actually there in any form and that I am certifiably mad."

Scenes from the *Fight Club* movie keep running through my head.

"I'm sorry, it's not that I don't believe that you are God. I am just having trouble processing everything right now and the more I can convince myself that you are living and breathing, the more I can embrace what you're saying to me."

"You are doing pretty well so far. Most people I've spoken with never get past the first sentence without calling me a liar or becoming violent."

I remember doing both.

"That's right, you were violent to me, but in your violent haze you wanted to be hugged, to be loved. I could feel you crying out. In fact you were crying out so loud I think the entire universe felt you. I knew we would get this far when I first looked into your eyes. That's why I came to you. The universe needs the love you can share. Now you want confirmation about what kind of being you are standing in front of."

I nod - yes. Lifting his shirt out of his pants and unbuttoning the three remaining buttons it had left, in the one quick motion, he quickly exposes his chest and belly. He is in fighter's shape. Where does he work out? I can see bruises on his ribs, probably from my assault the night before. I also count no fewer than four lesions that are definitely infected. His chest hair is sparse but matted by a combination of dried body sweat, dirt and dropped food. Then there are the scars – perhaps made by a knife? Puncture wounds, two near his neck, one splitting his left nipple in two, and one in particular two inches long, halfway down on the right side of the rib cage, looks like it is sewn up with a spoon. It looks terrible.

"Touch it."

"Touch what?"

"The scar you seem so interested in."

My hand trembles a bit. The scar tissue feels like dried rubber cement and it had that lighter-than-the-skin-around-it look to it.

"It was hard to sew it closed."

"You did that?"

"Yeah, I did. I was hurting, blood everywhere, it was dark, and all I had was a travel sewing kit I found in a hotel Dumpster. You ever try to thread a needle? When I finally

103

got the darn thing threaded, I pinched too much skin together, and when it healed it had a pretty big bump. I thought it would go down after the infection and swelling ceased, but it just stayed like you see it."

He takes a deep breath. His lungs swell with air, and his chest expands. The scar stretches. I fear the rubber cement may not hold.

"I think the knife hit my lung or something. Listen."

He grabs my head and places it on his chest. He inhales deeply again. I can hear odd emphysema shallowness to the expansion of his right lung. I don't know much about anything medical but he was right, it didn't sound good. He grabs my head again and slides it to the center of his chest between his nipples.

"How's the ticker sound?"

"I guess it's good. I can hear it pounding."

"Good news, not ready to evolve quite yet and to answer your question: yes I am human. I was with you last night. I have been following you around for months and ..."

"And what?"

"And I am God."

"That still is so hard to hear."

"It is hard to say, too. I'm not the boastful type."

"No, the fact that you're standing here; no white robes or golden glow, no levitating – nothing deity-like."

"All theater."

These chunks of conversation are just so hard to process. He spins, back to me, now facing the wall, un-holsters his penis and begins to urinate.

"Do you have any other questions about me being human or real?"

"I think that just about covers it."

His urine stream snakes its way between his feet and is heading toward my shoes. He finishes and spins back, adjusting his shirt, pants and fly stepping through the urine.

"Smell that?"

All I can smell is wet ass, piss, and exhaust.

"Smell what?"

"Freshly brewed coffee. Hey, I can't wait to walk all the way to Starbucks. I know a different place that is closer than Starbucks down here. Let's go this way."

He points down the opposite direction of the alley back toward shit city.

"It's a great place that gives me free coffee if I promise to leave."

16

I shouted, "THIS IS GOD!"

I start to find my bearings. We have walked from my office park to the sketchy part of downtown, referred to as 'Maundy's. I don't know where the name came from. I think she was a popular whore in the area. We are walking toward places people drive out of their way to avoid. I guess we have walked 15 miles. I have never walked this far in my life. Come to think of it, I really can use a cup of coffee, though - and a shower.

We cross a street lined with warehouses, with railroad tracks down the middle half covered over with asphalt. We are now in the seediest part of the city where most buildings are boarded or burned out. I don't think I ever drove down here much less had the pluck to walk this neighborhood.

It is an all black neighborhood with a few blocks of Hispanic families. From what little I can see, I dare not stare, most of the retailers are Korean by the looks of the people unlocking their heavily secured store fronts. Check cashing stores, pawn shops, and liquor stores fuel what economy is here. The soundtrack to a shithole neighborhood is screaming babies, barking dogs, music through cheap speakers and an occasionally back firing car or perhaps a gunshot. Suburbanites always think banging noises in the urban areas are gunshots. Most notable is us: the only two white people within miles, one dressed like a eighth-grade schoolteacher in khakis and the other a bum. For the first time I wish I was dressed like he was. I look like a mark. He looks like he belongs.

We reach "Mo Black Coffee Shop." The name is poorly painted, by hand, over an old RC Cola sign of a bygone era. The place was one of those old 1960's style, white tiled, coffee shops or ten cent hamburger joints: White Castle or Top Hat with the entire interior made from brushed aluminum or stainless steel and the floor covered in little, white ceramic tiles with an occasional black tile to break up the boredom. Miniature stools that you have to squat in to sit line the counter.

"Get the fuck out of here!"

A huge voice fills the small restaurant. It is Mo Black, and he is clearly familiar with God.

"I don't want you fucking around here anymore. Get the fuck out."

I wish I were one of those black ceramic tiles right about now. This barn of a sweat-drenched black man with an apron and cocked sideways army-style, paper hat starts heading our way.

"I got money!"

I scream it; stopping him right in his tracks. What I do know is that the common color of all races is green.

"Cash motherfucker, we don't do plastic here."

"Got it."

I actually hold up a $20 bill for his approval as we make our way to the two end stools furthest away from Mo's flat skillet stove. The coffees are slid in front of us. My God leans his face over the piping black brew and inhales like you see in those stupid coffee commercials. The rotary phone rings on the wall. Mo's attention is diverted by a take-out order. Thankfully, the place settles down, ignoring us now.

"Thanks. This is really nice, drinking coffee, sitting inside where it's warm. Want to continue talking . . ."

He looks at Mo.

". . . quietly?"

He smirks, putting his finger to his lips when he says "quietly." Questions start popping into my head but one was extremely relevant based on our immediate surroundings.

"Why are people different in color?"

"People are not different in color."

"Have you met Big Mo over there? He and I are not the same color."

"You're funny. For your information, you were once all the same exterior color and you will be again someday. When people migrated to different parts of the world their bodies adapted. This is a great evolutionary gift; your ability to adapt to your environment. Why should humans be any different from all the other creatures? People closer to the sun, by the equator, have to deal with more intense sun. Their skin adapts to a darker hue to absorb the sun's rays, their hair tough in texture, so they didn't burn to death. People further away from the sun become pale so when the sun is out their bodies can absorb much more of it. Folks in the dessert areas, where water was less available, adjust their needs physically over thousands of years being able to go longer without a drink. People in intense cold evolve a tougher outer skin and on and on it goes."

"I have seen wars fought throughout the ages and most are fought because you physically adapted to a region on the planet and now were different in some way physically from others. When your curiosity finally had you exploring different parts of the world your different appearances scared you - and with fear comes hatred. You are just still too infantile to see past your skin and into your hearts, your souls, and your minds. Heck you and I and Mo bleed the same red blood. You are all the same through and through. The difference now is fear of each other. I felt your fear when we were walking here. You all brought that fear on yourselves. And with fear comes protective hate voiding a person of love."

"The white people brought the fear?"

"All people; you are all afraid of each other- NOW - because you are different, live in different places and have different lifestyle or beliefs. You build walls instead of villages. Presently you are like a simple animal on this subject. If you do not understand something you would prefer to destroy it. Eventually you will develop enough to appreciate the true person, the soul in all of you. Your bodies, whatever the shape, size or color will have little impact on how your fellow man will judge you. Right NOW, you all have evolved enough to figure out you were not an ape or a tree, but not enough to know that you are all together in this journey and your appearance has little to do with anything. Take this to the bank: There is only one race on this planet: the human race. You are all the same color-blood red, it pumps though all your veins. And as soon as you figure out the power of loving each other the quicker the world will become the place it should be."

"Why did you say 'NOW!' so aggressively?"

"Most humans walk around thinking they have developed to their highest form. As I told you last night, you are children wandering in a world you have yet to figure out. When you do develop that pea brain of yours…."

He knocks on my head.

"…. you will not quibble about where you live or what you look like. You will begin to appreciate the value of the other person, begin to live together in peace and in a few hundred thousand years most of the world's inhabitants will look similar to one another. That is why I said 'now' because I know you will all begin to treat each other better and live together. You will all blend as one. You all started out about the same color, and when you evolve you will all be the same color again."

"What color will we all be?"

"… always stuck on color."

"Sorry, just curious."

"Well, if it all stays on track: light caramel, dark brown hair, eyes will always vary but predominately brown. The mind, soul and spirit must and will evolve then the physical features will follow after. When you stop judging each other on color of skin, hair or eyes, you will be drawn to each other's minds, your souls, your emotional and mental

109

attributes. You will step beyond the barriers of race, location, religion, and cohabitate and procreate. The world will lose color and religion as a reason to hate. It gets even better when your mind develops. You will know and share information on a mental plain and less of a physical one. Except for a small percentage of people, you will be warm, kind, loving, and accepting of each other."

"Automatically? We will just treat everyone really nicely because we are smarter?"

"We are about ready to move into an area that you will have a lot of trouble processing. But I will quickly try to keep it simple and then get back to the race thing. The power of love - and I mean the fuel, the energy of the universe - and the evolution of your spirit and your soul, feed and grow stronger with each other. The strength of love increases in power by how many people love and share your love. The more people that you love and who love you, the stronger the power you possess in the universe. This power, this strength, is what drives and expands the universe."

"Come on, the entire universe?"

"You know I'm probably here a few million years too early to discuss this, but you have NO idea what you are capable of and expected to do in this process. But know that the universe is expanding because you all are the energy that fuels it."

"Me?"

"You, Mo, species on other different worlds ... her, all energy."

He points to a woman sitting at a stool at the other end of the counter.

"Once you figure out that the strength, vastness and velocity of your next existence grows with the combined power of your love for one another, you will stop hating and hurting each other because the more strength you gain from one another, the greater your next journey will be."

"Greater?"

"When I brought you to your wife you became one energy, one soul, twice the power source. Imagine that sharing ability with all the people you have loved on earth. Imagine the power thousands of you would possess as one unit. It could expand a universe."

"Huh?"

"I will explain more later but I will finish this point by saying that the small percentage people that hate and do not love or join together with others now, will be extremely limited to their opportunities in the next evolution."

"I am foggy as hell on what I think love is and what you are trying to explain to me what love is. Love, like I have for my wife."

"Let me see if I can back up here and clarify."

> God stirs his coffee with his shortened ring finger: a knob, no nail. I can see him trying to mentally ratchet down the information allowing me to understand it.

"Okay let's try this. Since the beginning of human time when you stood up and began to walk, but more importantly began to think and deduce, you had this inner desire, a natural instinct to be curious, search for new things, discover, to learn to dream. Since the beginning of human time when you cast your eyes to the skies you wondered why, who am I, and how do I fit in? To this day you are driven to figure how you fit - if at all - into the big picture, the expanding universe."

"Oddly, and what you haven't figured out yet, is that the answers to your questions of 'Who am I?' and 'How do I fit into the master plan that is the expanding universe?' are also inside of you. The same internal desire that drives you to be curious is also the desire that drives you to love, to be drawn to each other, to grow together, have families, expand the human race... because that passion you have is also the answer to the expanding universe. The curiosity you have for the unknown is the same emotional compass that points you toward loving. Because the more you love the more energy you will have and greater part you will play in the expanding universe."

"Lost me."

"Figured. I'll try one more time. That lump in your gut, the one that almost drove you to suicide when your wife passed, the one you call love here on earth is also the natural trigger that drives your curiosity to find out the answers to the whys in the universe. And what you will eventually find is that this internal angst, this uneasiness, this passion to explore, to wonder, to love, is all the same thing. In your mental infancy you have

separated the two, one being important science, the other being love for a partner. It's not separate; it is all the same thing that drives you."

"What do you mean, it's the same thing, it doesn't feel like the same thing?"

"Well, that's where your mental development stops you from figuring it out, but that will change over centuries."

God lowers his voice to a whisper, sets his chin on my shoulder and leans in to my ear.

"One: The reason you are so curious about the big universe questions is because inside you …."

He touches my chest and stomach.

"… you know instinctively you have a greater journey, a responsibility to be part of the expanding universe. You just don't know the plan, the course and how you are involved."

"The underdeveloped factor?"

"Yes. Two: What you also haven't figured out yet is that the answers to the questions of the universe are also inside you: you call love, your desire for another person or persons. That desire to become more than one, to have a family is the same fuel that drives your curiosity and the entire universe's expansion. Your 'love' as you describe it here on earth, is the energy of the big bang and the presently expanding universe."

"Three: When you share 'love' as you put it, with many others the more your energy increases when it is shared. The more people that you love the greater the power you possess. So when you evolve, you will possess more energy, more power, more…"

"Love?"

"Yes, love. Now you're starting to get it, you just labeled it to only perceive it as an emotional feeling you have toward one another. It is just the tip of your iceberg that you haven't put your arms around yet. What you call love is energy. So these gut feelings you have here and here…"

He touches my chest and stomach again.

".... are just your eventual destiny trying to press you into wanting to develop, to grow intellectually and emotionally so you can fulfill your place in the expanding universe and use the energy to evolve and become part of the big bang that still is banging. Why do salmon swim upstream to spawn then die. They don't know but they are driven to do it. You're salmon right now."

"Okay, so forget the fish. Are you saying that's why people will dismiss hate, because it will benefit them in their future?"

"No, they will dismiss hate and love one another because that's what is right and will feel right to them by nature. If I remember correctly, you know what love is with your wife. Imagine that happening with everyone in the world. It will be your natural, human instinct. It is the fabric of the soul. You are just too undeveloped to process this yet. Think how much better your day would have been if we had walked through that door and Mo had hugged us and gave us a nice cup of hot coffee. You would have met a new friend and offered a big tip, because you take care of friends."

"You would have felt comfortable here, not afraid of the neighborhood or anyone in it. You would have returned the hug with a warm handshake and a smile. Love would well up in your hearts because you are better, wiser, larger, knowing each other. With your power and your strength together, your spirits, your souls would expand your love for everyone around you. Euphoria would be palpable in this room. He would introduce you to his friends and you yours. Strangers would feel it and join in on the conversations. A celebration of loving souls would ensue, singing and dancing, strengthening all your spirits together. You would all become enriched by each other. And throughout the process no one, and I mean no one, would care if they were man or woman, black or white, Chicano or Hispanic, tall, short, skinny, fat, rich or poor. Love judges no one. Love embraces everyone. Love is the power of the universe."

His eyes close. He drifts off to a light sleep, head resting on my shoulder. I sit there and finishing my coffee wishing I was in the place he described.

"You muthafuckers can't sleep in here! This ain't no flop house! You have to order food or fucking leave."

Ah, reality. Mo slams his catcher glove-sized hand on the other end of the counter, waking up God. I guess Mo didn't hear the last part of God's speech.

Talk to God

"Two burgers and fries, loaded."

God yawns...

"...and I'll have a refill on my coffee please?"

The big man grabs the pot from the heating plate and walks over, cartwheeling a tooth pick in his mouth with his tongue. His voice sounded like a gravel hauler.

"What are you, his case worker or P.O? Did he tell 'you' who he thinks he is?"

"No."

My God shoots me a surprised look of disbelief. For the first time I see sadness wash over his face. Mo presses me, as if trying to save me the psycho-babble.

"He didn't tell you that he was God?"

I am frightened thinking what Mo might do to me if I tell him what I think.

"Nope, just a couple of guys sitting here shooting the breeze."

"Well fucking ask him who he thinks he is!"

"I would prefer not to."

Mo looks at God and sneers.

"Go ahead, tell him who you think you are."

"He knows who I am and believes me."

"You believe him muthafucker?"

"No, well,"

114

I pause, tongue dries, pulse racing.

"I don't know."

Mo walks away laughing.

"Burgers and fries for God and the cracker! Ha,ha,ha."

"You don't believe I am God?"

"What do you want from me? Do you want me to get my ass kicked? We're going to get thrown out of here. Do you want me to tell people you are God? Don't you want to finish your coffee and eat the food I ordered you?"

"Is that what is important to you: food?"

"I am shredded. I have lost my wife, life as I know it BLOWS, and I am now following a homeless man, who's God, who changed my life last night, giving me back my wife for a few hours…"

I pause as I hear the words pass my lips: –

"giving me back my wife for a few hours."

I drift back to memories of my wife last night. Rage, not tears wash through me. What the fuck am I doing? I am totally embarrassed. Stop acting like a chicken shit. Man up!

"Mo !"

I increase my tone. He isn't paying attention

" MO!"

"Whatchu want, cracker?"

I stand up straddling my stool, making me look shorter than usual. I clear my throat.

115

Talk to God

"This IS God!"

I am screaming now.

"Wha chu'say?"

Silence blankets the diner. All eyes turn to watch the expected carnage. I shouted again.

"THIS IS GOD!"

My eyes are fixed to Mo's. I stare at him, daring not to blink. He stares back. My left knee is trembling. Hold it together. Is it five seconds? It seems an eternity. He wipes his brow with his forearm, Mexican stand-off. The phone rings. He turns his back to us and walks toward the phone.

"Two crazy white boys. Get yo' money ready. When I set dese burgers down in front of you, you're payin', eatin' fast, and gettin' yo' Jehovah Witness asses outta here. Fuckin' white assholes. God? And who are you, Moses? Michael Jordan...?"

He walks away pointing at each person sitting at the counter.

"And here is Al Green, Michael Jackson, nah you too dark, Mike Tyson, and this fucker here with the wave is Al Sharpton! Ha, ha, ha!"

He points to the mailman sitting near the door with his natural hair straightened and combed back. Everyone at the counter has a good laugh at the two white people sitting at the end of the counter.

We eat in silence. I know I hurt God's feelings, but I also know he was impressed when I recanted. Where did that burst of defiance come from? I don't know. It sure wasn't my style. Maybe I was just sleep deprived, frightened by my surroundings, but I felt strong and powerful neither traits I have possessed in the past. This weekend full of surprises continues.

116

Watching God eat is grotesque. He shovels food into his mouth without chewing. When he finishes he cleans his plate by picking it up and licking the pooled burger grease from the beveled center, then takes the ketchup bottle and squirts what probably is two full ounces on his licked clean plate, salts the ketchup and licks that too, off his plate. Before I take one bite of my burger and fries, he has feverishly inhales his burger and fries, and now two ounces of ketchup for dessert. I slow my eating purposely and do not eat half of my hamburger nor my fries.

"Do you want my…"

Before I can get the invitation out of mouth, to finish my food he grabs my burger and fries and jams it into his side pocket. No bag, napkin, or container, just fries and hamburger in his left Army jacket pocket with who knows what.

"Ready to go?"

"Yeah, I'm ready. We can get a bag to go for that food."

117

17

"No: Though shall not kill, mess around with another man's wife,
Though shall not steal -none of that?"

"No worries."

"Where to?"

The twenty on the counter allows us to leave Mo Black
Coffee without any mo conflicts or criticisms from Mo. I think the bill was
eleven bucks. Some tip for all that wonderful service. I feel empowered
though. I feel good. I feel proud of myself. And when my wife's memory
came up in our little discussion back at the coffee shop, my heart didn't
break. In fact, I now don't ache for her dead memories, I think about
seeing her again very soon.

"How about walking to one of my favorite places?"

"How far? My feet are getting a little sore."

"Well it's a bit, but what a great day for a walk."

He is right. I find myself appreciating the weather. It's
been a while. Now this goes back to just when she got cancer.
Blue skies are wasted when someone you love is dying. You just
don't care to notice. And when you do notice the majesty of the

day you wish you hadn't because you don't dare share a great weather story with someone you know will never see the outside of the building they were dying in. But today the breeze is soft and warm, the sky newborn, baby blue. With one very large inhale, I try to suck in as much fresh morning air as I possibly can. I feel awake, fed, happy, and the big one: alive again.

"So, God has nothing to do with the weather?"

"Sorry, I would love to take credit for this weather, but before you know it you will be shoveling snow and cursing me. Now, in a broader sense I created the universe, so I guess I make the weather, but not like you are thinking: choosing the climate or temperature day to day. The earth is on auto pilot."

We begin walking silently, interrupted only by large and loud burps from God, reminding me of how we used to try to get a girl's attention back in the fifth grade. Roy Dunnam could burp the alphabet in one breath. I think he got the girl. I really wish God would act more God-like. It would make the journey a lot more believable.

"Maybe you shouldn't gulp your food."

No response. One more burp and a follow-up swallow.

"Can we talk about religion?"

I got God's attention. God shoots me a look and rolls his eyes.

"Sure. I hope I don't disappoint you."

"I don't think you can."

"We'll see. Fire away."

"You sent the 10 commandments down to Moses on Mt. Sinai as the rules of the world for humans to live by and..."

He interrupts.

119

Talk to God

"No I didn't."

"NO?"

"No."

"No: Though shall not kill, mess round with another man's wife, though shall not steal - none of that?"

"Nope"

"Seriously?"

"Seriously. How do you have free will and then send down a rule book? Plus the whole commandments thing was so not me. I command nothing from people. Humans must decide what's right or wrong on their own, and from those actions come their eventual future. The Ten Commandments were written by man, pure and simple as the law of the times. By the way, they are pretty good rules, but they are not my rules. They were the rules used to govern a restless crowd."

"Egypt was the center of the universe at the time, the Israelites were bailing and their leaders needed some muscle to keep a hungry crowd from going nuts, and nothing says pay attention better than some scary stuff from God to keep the pagans in line."

"So no Commandments?"

"No, there are commandments, but you made them up and your religions work to get people to follow them. But they weren't from me. If you love you wouldn't do any of those things the commandments tells you not to do."

I look shocked, my face flush.

"I guess you did disappoint me."

"Religion, when peeled back to its core has a tendency to do that. But don't get all depressed. Would you like to know the rules I did give every human being on the planet to govern them while they are here and beyond?"

"Yes! Yes! Of course!"

"Let's start by thinking about these rules on a commonsense level. I know it's odd for religions to portray commonsense but bear with me. For instance, God, the master of the universe, would not send down a rule book to keep the Israelites in check, then slaughter the bad guys with a Red Sea water trick. Come on! Does that sound like any other Supreme Being. I let some people live and wipe out the others. I would lose my Supreme Being membership card. And why wouldn't I send down the rules thousands of years earlier? Did I not think that humans before that didn't need rules? Seems a little presumptive and quite handy for the Jews wanting to leave Egypt."

"If I wanted some rules, I would make the rules, the recommendations, or, for the sake of you getting this, my commandments, hardwired into every human."

"Why didn't you?"

"I did."

"Really"

"The so-called rules are part of the physical, spiritual, and mental makeup of every human, and for that matter, every living creature. That I explained to you at Mo's. You have your so-called rules right now, right inside you."

"I've have been given rules? And I have them? Right now?"

"Yep, the rules have been there in all living creatures since Adam and Eve if there were Adam and Eve."

"All living creatures needed my rules, not rules, some framing well before Moses."

"So what are they?"

"The rules are based on the purest and simplest of loves that hold humanity together."

"The love that powers the universe?"

"Same source in your gut; it is the origin of life, passion, protection. It is inside all of you. It is a constant love that's immeasurable, love that blossoms and flourishes, and its strength is what guides all creatures here and throughout the universe and beyond."

Talk to God

"What is it?"

God slows his walk, grabs my forearm, and spins me so we are face to face and smiles a huge, wide grin.

"It is a mother's love for her child."

"A mother's love comprises all the rules? I was expecting some commandments."

"Stay with me. The center of all the energy in the universe is a woman and her love. You men have been told this throughout time and your egos won't let you get out of the way. The woman is the origin of life, the nurturer, the provider and the protector. She covets all. Her love – my - rules are passed from her to her children, beginning in the womb and lasting until death."

"What rules?"

"You are such a guy. The connection, the love between a mother and her child are the only real 'rules.' The lessons begin prior to birth with the ultimate bond of being inside the woman. Upon birth, the separation of the mother and child is catastrophic for both. The birth, or first separation of the two, increases the intensity of the love since they have lost the common, shared, thread of one life supporting two. Both instinctively crave to be one again. Through birth and through childhood, the intensity of love is unwavering. The child feels and reacts to the mother's touch, her warmth, her sound. Their hearts beat in unison. They are inseparable. The message of unconditional love is passed to the child; the next generation. This is how every person starts their life and sees the world, as I do: through the loving eyes of their mother."

"So what are the rules?"

"I'm sorry that you and your wife never experienced having a baby, so I won't rail you on your male perspective. The rules of natural love are as follows: Everyone should treat each other like they are treated by their mother."

"That's it? I know some people that will tell you that their mothers are a pain in the ass."

"Oh yeah, but go ahead and say something bad about someone's mother and see what happens. Or go ask any mother: Would they give their lives for their child? A mother

would do anything to protect her children, anything. This is an extremely powerful connection that is shared by every creature and their offspring on earth and in other places. This is the only real rule needed and it's not a rule, it's in your wiring, it's your nature. When I want humans to have rules I hardwire them right into your melon."

"So the rules are 'love' you get from your mom?"

"Yes. But you are not getting this, are you? The internal bond between a mother and child is unwavering. The problem today is for many; the rules fade, or are not popular, but they still exist in everyone. Now, that is not to say there are instances where a woman is mentally handicapped or has melted her brain with drug addiction and cannot feel or share the natural love in their heart, but ninety nine out of one hundred woman do. As soon as you start treating everyone like you were treated by your mother and how you respond in return, the world will become a loving place where there will be only love. Show me a mother and I will show you a person who would lay down their life for their child."

"I was expecting 'thou shall not kill' type rules."

"They are all there. Would you kill someone if your mom was standing there? Would you screw the neighbor wife while your mom was watching you? Would you be kind to people if your mother asked you to? Would you swear around your mom? Would you do anything needed to protect your mother from sickness or harm? Would you steal if your mom were to find out? Make sure you are extremely clear about this: A mother's love is the center of the universe and responsible for its growth. When we begin to treat everyone like a mother treats her child or a child treats his mother, all wars will end, there will be no crime, there would be no more suffering."

"Think about women when they mature. Who is the romantic? Who is the one that forgives? Who plans for the family? Who does all the nesting? Who is always the first falling in love? And once a woman chooses her special partner, she takes him inside her heart, her soul, and her body. Men are driven to be accepted, loved, and nurtured just like they were by their mothers, and they want the feeling back. The center of the universe is the love of a woman, a mother. Those are God's only rules and they are powerful and perfect. No other rules are required."

Well I didn't see that coming. I think I should press on. You can tell the mother thing is extremely important to him and thinking about it; it is.

123

18

Just kidding. Good Question. Good news:
You're talking to the person named Jesus Christ right now.

"Okay, no Ten Commandments. We are born with natural rules, and women are the center of the universe and control everything?"

"Not control: nurture. Don't sound so melancholy. You knew the rules. I just reminded you of them. Did you really believe the commandments were sent down to a mountain top, to one guy, alone, then, some of the boys in his crew decide to build a gold altar fashioned to look like a goat to use for sacrifices to God? Moses comes down with the 10 commandments, sees the goat, and throws the 10 commandments he just got from God at the altar and smashes the stone tablets. So what does he do next?"

"I don't know?"

"Moses goes back up the mountain, alone, and gets an extra carbon copy from God like an extra set of car keys. Come on! No Commandments. Next question."

"I am a little nervous to ask this one after you trashed the Ten Commandments."

"Don't be bashful."

"Was there a Jesus?"

"I have been visiting earth for generations. Sometimes I become an integral part of the culture and what I say gets picked up, written down, and taught to generations to come. And there are other times I get clipped before I can share the truth about love and the universe and never make a mark. Maybe you should ask about Noah's Ark?"

"Why?"

"Just kidding. You are talking to the person named Jesus Christ now."

"You? You are …?"

"Were…"

"Jesus Christ?"

"Yes."

"JESUS CHRIST! You were Jesus Christ?"

"Funny. Hold on, let's start with some framing. Actually I am God, I visit Earth often. I like being here. If I choose, I will be born and live a life teaching about loving each other in the universe, how it all works, and 2,000 years ago I was here and my mom named me Jesus. For whatever the reason, when I was talking back then people noticed, paid attention, and wrote a lot of stuff down."

"Yeah they wrote a lot of stuff down. They wrote the New Testament."

"Well it was an interesting time and more like 300 years later before they started putting all that phooey in book form. The simple folks back then couldn't process God running the universe and also standing in front of them at the same time. It was a lot to deal with. And you think you are not mentally developed."

I still don't know if I have dealt with the fact that I am a spiritual, emotional, and physical moron. God, I feel stupid.

"So I came up with this concept that I was God's son. It allowed them to think of God like they have been: big booming voice out of the clouds, and also be able to listen so they could appreciate my teachings. Probably not the best move, but I got to tell you, it

125

worked. There are things in the New Testament they got right, mostly the love parts. All the other crap was crap, plenty of poetic license."

My brain starts spinning; my knees are rubbery. He sees me losing it.

"Maybe we should sit down and not worry about poetic license."

He chuckles as he grabs my arm and escorts me to a blue, plastic milk crate against the wall of a convenience store. Bars protect the bulletproof glass windows. It looks more like a cinder block bunker with a few weatherworn, vinyl, beer banners littering the facade of the building. I sat and took a few long breaths. He stands next to me against the wall then slides down, plopping himself right next to me on the sidewalk.

"Better?"

I nodded my approval, but I was lying.

"When I was speaking to those people back in 20 A.D. it is just like I am speaking to you now. The difference between now and then is they really were in their formative stages as humans and had trouble believing me, like someone else I know. Hell, they were praying to the weather."

"You really are Jesus Christ?"

I put my head between my knees and started to breath heavy.

"I was at that time."

"So this is the end?"

"What do you mean the end? Are you going to be able to hold it together?"

Gasping for air now, I see my childhood prayers flashing through my head.

126

"You know that thousands, millions, billions of Christians are awaiting your return to judge the living and the dead."

"I am not here to judge anybody living in any form. What will be a shock to everyone, is that no one is really dead as you understand it, so why judge them. It's not the end of the world or something. That's was a religious fear tactic so everyone played nice. It's not true. As I said, I come here all the time. I haven't missed any big events and love watching you all evolve and having coffee with Mo."

"Just so I get this straight. You are God and you visit the earth as a man......"

"Or woman. Sound familiar?"

"... or woman, and back around 2 B.C."

"Yeah but they didn't call it B.C. or A.C. Hell, I don't know if many people knew what year it was. There weren't many educated people. Not a lot of readers."

"Get back to what I am trying to figure out. You were born into a family, your mom named you Jesus, and you started walking around preaching."

"Preaching is a little formal. I was doing what we are doing right now: I was talking to people."

"So this isn't the end of the world?"

"No! The world ends here in five billion years give or take a couple million years. That's when the sun goes out. Actually the sun evolves, too, but that is when things will change around here. But when that time comes, that change will be celebrated. You will be controlling minds by then, and it will be cool! You will count down the moment like you do for New Year's Eve now!"

"But if the sun goes out we all die!"

"Evolve."

"Right."

127

"You evolve and that is why by then you will know what that means and you ALL will be very excited about the process."

"Okay, so let's get back to you being here all the time. If you are here all the time, why hasn't religion changed? Why haven't you told them the stuff you are telling me?"

"I try to tell them that I am here and how it really is. I can't tell you how many times I have reached out to the big wheels in all the churches and they shoo me away, threatening to call the authorities. Classic, wouldn't you say, the church has God arrested."

God stops speaking. As we sit, he wrenches his arm entangling it into mine swinging it to the left and pointing.

"You walk over there and YOU tell them."

I look up from my milk crate, noticing that our walk has landed us across the street from the largest church in the metropolitan area: St. Michael's Cathedral. The pope said mass there. Three U.S. Presidents have attended services there and if something religious is happening in the news, they get their sound bites from holy-roller central, right across the street.

"I can't help noticing that we just so happen to be here … now. Irony? Trying to prove a point?"

"You can always use a prop, and you wanted to talk religion. Those boys…."

He points to the church again.

"… and that's the worst part; only boys, have a great paying gig over there selling fear and eternal life. Do you really think they want to hear the truth? Do you really think they want everything they believe in that makes up 'their' church to change? Do you really think they want to stop collecting money or letting the true leaders of God, the women, in to run the joint?"

God gets up and walks to the edge of the street, toes the curb, leans out facing the facade of the cathedral across the street, cups his mouth with his hands and screams.

"If that is a church you have built for me, all you hustlers, tax collectors, liars, money changers, pedophiles, snake-oil salesmen who are running that hustle, should leave my church! Let the truth about love set you and everyone around you free!"

No one notices God. Ranting, homeless men are abundant here. He begins to repeat his speech when the cathedral bells toll, drowning him out. He lowers his head, sad for a moment, then a wily smirk replaces his sadness.

"Ah forget about it."

He starts back toward me when something clicks nearly visibly in God's head. He hikes his shoulders, places his elbows against his ribs, and begins pointing invisible guns while making a wrinkled face.

"Hey you…fuggedaboutit!"

God's doing his best Marlon Brando, mafia guy impression. He begins belly laughing.

"I love that bit. Did I sound like a gangster? I saw it in a movie. When the bad guys say fuggedaboutit, which really means you are still okay with the family. So, hey you…"

He faces the church.

"Fuggedaboutit!! I have returned… again and it's NOT the end of the world, and I am not judging you today or anyone else today or any other day. It's not going to happen. Love one another! It's free will today and until the very end, so fuggottaboutit!!"

He has trouble stopping his laughter. He walks back toward me still doing his Brando. The laughter is contagious, and I feel much better. He grabs me by my shoulders and stands me up, dragging me back up the brick wall, all the while still laughing. Now I am laughing with him. We continue our walk, giggling like two kids.

"Was that your favorite place?"

"Nah, we still have a ways to go."

129

Talk to God

"Okay, so back up. You're are here all the time?"

"Yes. And sometimes I choose to be heard, but most of the time I like just fitting in and watching you all grow."

"But how does it work. Do you grow up starting as a baby like every other human or do you just appear as an adult every generation?"

"I stem cell, clone myself in."

He pauses, grins awaiting my reaction.

"Really?"

"Gotcha!"

More laughter.

"Just kidding. I am born and live my life just like everyone else and here is what is a mystery for me, I keep coming back because I just think about coming back when I am..."

"Am what?"

"When I am being killed and dying, I think about coming back and next thing you know I am a baby again. It is one of God's true mysteries ... to God! That is probably the only thing I can't explain to you today. I am sure it has something to do with the energy I possess and receive from loving."

More unbridled laughter.

"Do you choose your situation?"

"Not really. It doesn't matter. I do like to be orphaned or homeless. It puts me in the trenches earlier with no money or family support. I usually have a pretty steady game plan. I teach as many people as I can while I am here, evaluate your growth and evolution, then I get loud and aggressive with my teachings, someone gets mad and kills me because they don't like what I say. Then I start all over again or visit other places."

130

"Really? Pretty morbid."

It is the down side of coming and speaking against the current of society's religious beliefs. I figure the time I come here and die of old age instead of being killed, we will be getting closer to a fully developed human brain. Right now you are a lot like the simple beasts that roam the earth. If you don't understand it... you kill it. In this case the one you don't yet understand and kill is me.

"Sorry"

I felt I needed to apologize on behalf of the entire human race.

It's okay.

131

19
*"Did you know you were going to be killed that night
in front of the Dakota Apartment in New York?"*

God shrugs and laughs.

"Can humans reincarnate?"

*"Nope, when you see where your wife is and where you will go, there's no coming back.
You wouldn't want to and you do not have the ability to. You evolve to such an
enormous energy you couldn't come back if you want to. I just have the misfortune of
having the ability to do the reappearing God trick."*

"Did I know any other people you came as?"

"You mean besides Jesus?"

"Yeah."

Blush reddens God's checks and near his neck by his
collar bone and collar line. I can tell he is uneasy; embarrassed;
nervous? He looks uneasy.

"What?"

"You probably did know one other of the people."

"Like a pope! Or, I got it: Mother Theresa!"

"No, I don't run with fake religions but Mother Theresa was beyond religion, she was the goods. I like to be judged as a regular man, not a man of the cloth as you say. I can reach and touch more people without the mask of religion. How far would we have gotten if I were a priest."

"Good point, so who? Who have you been that I might have known?"

"Fuggittabboutit, will ya?"

"No come on, it will help me process."

"Lennon."

"Marks and Lenin, Lenin?"

"No."

"John Winston, probably named after Churchill ......Ono........Lennon."

"You mean John Lennon; The Beatle?"

"Yes."

"John fucking Lennon! That's cooler than being Jesus! You got… to be shitting me! "

"Nope."

"John Lennon? Get the fuck out of here!"

"Yep. It wasn't meant to be like that; being famous, but I did reach a ton of people to tell the truth that go-around. Actually I never expected the fame to happen. On the contrary, it was a horrible time to be born in a horrible neighborhood to low income parents. My dad was a merchant marine sailor and my mom was never around. I really had a rough start that time around."

"When was it?"

"I was born in Liverpool, in October 1940, in the middle of a German air raid. Talk about some shitty formative years. I didn't think I would ever make it out of there alive as a small child. I just remember the sirens and the noise of the bombs exploding and the screams. My parents disappeared early in my life and I bounced from aunt to family friends all of my young life. When I got into my teen years I was an art major and a poet in advanced levels of education. I dropped out of the university to start a band. I got the idea for a band when I saw Elvis Presley and the millions of young people he was reaching with his music. I thought 'this may be a way to get kids and young adults out of the churches to hear the real story of love and their future. I couldn't name the band for the life of me."

"It was the Beatles, right?"

"Well eventually, that was name number eight. I named the band The Black Jacks, The Quarry Men, Johnny and the Moondogs, The Beatals with an 'a', the Silver Beatles, the Silver Beats, then The Beatles, then back to The Silver Beatles, then finally The Beatles."

"Hey, didn't President Nixon want to deport you for speaking out against war?"

"Yeah, and I loved the attention. The more he complained about me, the more the young people liked what I was saying. I touched a lot of people with the music. It was probably the most visible of all the times I have come back. The explosion of the television media fueled the message."

"So when you got in trouble for saying; 'we're more popular than Jesus Christ', you were actually telling the truth and speaking from experience?"

"Yeah; plus everyone who believed in Jesus also were told to believe in religion. But compared to the last number of times I was back on earth, that time I 'was' bigger than Jesus Christ ever was, I should know, I was here as Jesus."

"Was it a slip what you said about Jesus Christ?"

"Nope, I don't slip on the important stuff. I wanted to draw attention to me; or God. I brought God and Jesus Christ to the front of the main stream media. It made people think."

"Can I ask you some questions that aren't God questions?"

"Beatles fan?"

I nodded yes!

" Sure."

"Did Yoko really break up the Beatles?"

My God bellows a huge blast of a laugh.

"Nope. Truth be told, George did. I loved when George evolved. I actually was with him. He looked at me and said; 'It's you! I always thought what you were talking about was bollix, but you were telling the truth.' We hugged, laughed and cried for hours but he was the Beatle that began the end of the group. Paul and I were pretty much controlling the creative direction. George got one song to write and sing lead on each album. Check it out. And Paul and I would write one song on each album for Ringo to sing within one or two notes of middle 'C'; that was his vocal range. We could have released double albums, heck triple albums, every record. We had that much material."

"George was writing some amazing songs; we all were heading toward the end, on our own, but George said he was leaving to write and record his own stuff first. He said what we all were thinking first. After that, little by little, we all moved onto our solo careers even before we released 'Let It Be'."

" I also needed the space to get on track to do what I came to do. Paul was very driven by pop fame and fortune. We had built the audience, now I had to teach the world about love. Listen to almost every song I wrote after the Beatles."

"Did you know you were going to be killed that night in front of the Dakota Apartments in New York?"

"I knew it was going to be around that time. I rarely live past 40. Looking back at that go around, the problem of getting killed and being famous and loved by millions is that it effects many people and hurts many people. It was a present day crucifixion but that is how I always go."

"What about the guy that killed you?"

"No style. He said years later he was going to kill me or Johnny Carson. It was an odd night. I actually was pretty pumped about the latest stuff I was recording. Mark David Chapman, who killed me, was lurking outside my apartment for a couple of days. I always made myself accessible to meet people. I could walk around New York and not get hassled. The day he killed me, we spoke a few hours before. He asked for an autograph. I gave it to him and he just stared at me. I stared into his eyes. He and I knew what he was supposed to do. You could see the pain in his eyes. If I were to hug him I could have changed him, but I thought it was time to move on. He just didn't know he was about to kill God."

"So I asked him, 'is the only thing you want is an autograph'? Do you need money? What is it you came to do? I thought I would dare him? He just froze. I thought I startled him with the question. I guess he was getting cold feet. So I asked him again, with a firmer voice; 'what is it you came to do?' I stared into his eyes. He knew, I knew what he was about to do. He reminded me of Judas; a bitter lost soul. How does a child get that twisted inside his head? He wasn't right: a bad mix of genes. Not everyone is lucky to get a good skill package. I really wanted to hold him, to tell him it's going to be alright. It's a shame, but he didn't do it then. Chicken I guess."

"From what I gathered reading about it a while back, he stayed around the front door until I returned that evening. I was walking into the apartment right past him; again. I stared at him. Everything went into slow motion; it always does with murder. I gave him a look that would have frightened anyone. I wanted to get this thing over with. I got about three steps pasts him. Then I heard this childlike voice, 'Mr. Lennon'? I stopped and before I could turn around; bang, bang, bang. The chicken shit shot me in the back. I guess he couldn't handle my staring at him. He fired six bullets at me, five hit me and I was dying sloppily. That was hard on Yoko. Blood was everywhere. It was coming out of my mouth. That always looks creepy. I fell flat on my face."

"I am losing consciousness and all I can hear is screaming and sirens. The last thing I remember a New York City police officer picks me up and fireman's carries me to his squad car. When he and I fall into the back seat and he unfolded my weakening body from over his shoulder, he looked into my eyes, he whispered; Hang on."

"I smiled at him and shook my head no. I was losing all strength. I remember when he was carrying me, I wondered if that is what a child felt like when a dad picks up a son who has skinned his knee. It felt wonderful, safe comforting. It was one of the few times in my centuries of memories I felt the strength and love of a father holding me. It was nice."

"He slammed the door and jumped across the front hood of the squad, scrambling to get into the car. In one motion, he slammed his door, dropped the car into gear and wiped my blood from his brow. Checking to see if I was still alive he asked me: 'Do you know who you are?' I nodded yes and said; I am God. Then he said: 'Hang on son, hang on.'"

"Then I drifted away. My only sadness was leaving Yoko without a proper goodbye, but she knew it was about to happen."

"She knew you were God?"

"I told her and she said she believed me, but she loved me so much I think she would have believed anything I told her. It was one of the few times when I was here that I had someone to talk to about what I was doing. We did everything we could to lead by example, but looking back at the nude press conferences and the love-ins we were probably a little aggressive for the time but that has always been my style; big, loud, against the grain and always a target for a crucifixion or assassination."

God smiles widely not really caring; he talks of death like I talk about sports. The story casually rolls off his lips. I am aghast in utter amazement.

"Could you tell me the most interesting thing that ever happened to you when you were a Beatle?"

God, stops and puts his hand on his chin doing his best Rodin's, Thinker.

"Hmm, the boys were getting into a lot of different religious and spiritual awareness crap. We all went to India to study and meditate with the Maharishi. I like checking out the competition. I was taking LSD trying to figure out if the drug accelerated the maturity of the human brain."

"Did it?"

"No. It actually splintered what brain power you had at the present time in different, obtuse directions. But it did not unlock the vast brain capability or advance it."

"So let me finish. We think we are going over there to get spiritually uplifted and after a few LSD trips and a few laughs the freak, Maharishi told us he wanted to screw our wives and girlfriends as a religious act. What a dick. I don't even think he had game.

137

But that is so typical of religions. They use their power and position just to get off. He was a sham so we split."

"Last Beatles question."

"Shoot."

"Best music memory."

"We performed 'All You Need Is Love' in front of four hundred million television viewers world-wide June 25th 1967; at least they said there were four hundred million. That was the most people I ever touched in one moment to date. Love is all you need is the only true message. All You Need Is Love should be the world's anthem."

"So you wrote the song in an attempt to explain all that you are telling me now about the power of love. Shit! And everybody thought it was just a love song but was truly the key to the power of the expanding universe."

"Yep. And look who just caught up."

A wily smirk cross his expression. Finally getting something makes God proud of me. I guess that's better than me killing him if I didn't understand.

"Were you anyone else famous like Gandhi?"

"Nope; I am usually just an ordinary person."

"Yeah, ordinary."

20

*"Find a child who is abused, beaten and tortured
and hug them and feel the wealth of unused love
swell from their souls into yours."*

"Do you read newspapers?"

"After I am done using them for a blanket, I glance at them once in a while."

"Did you happen to notice the big stink about gay marriage? Where does God sit on gay marriage?"

"I think marriage in general as a human institution, or sacrament in religious circles is a bit overdone. An unbridled love that a person shares with another never should require a ceremony to validate their love and devotion for each other. True love is never ending and transcends your earthly lives. There is no need for ceremony when you are in love with your match, or matches, your soul mate, your ying to their yang. That bond is forever. Marriage narrows the ability for people to love many. I am not saying polygamy, but marriage has a way of shutting off your desire to reach to more people of any sex to love and share love. Love comes in many levels and should be embraced with everyone. Of course share more intense love with a chosen partner, but don't forget to love all. The idea of marriage as a sacrament and a ritual carried out in a church as 'to be married in God's eyes' is a bunch of foolishness. Love, true love between people as I told you, is a natural mechanism that drives humans to grow from generation to generation. I am not

watching every marriage, but more importantly the loved ones you surround yourself with are watching. That is where the strength is: your love together supported by your family and friends' love. By the way, I love weddings. The love flows between families; it's a great opportunity to share love. But the institution of marriage is not required and for sure I don't have to be there to make it real. Imagine me trying to get to millions of weddings on a Friday. I am too busy making sure people don't sin by eating meat on Friday."

He laughs.

"You know when I said 'gay marriage' that meant same sex marriages?"

(sarcastic) "Thank you."

"Sorry."

"Love; and not to beat a dead horse, fuels the growth and expansion of the universe. I didn't say who you are to love. I didn't say when or how. Love…"

He grabs his own lapels like he is holding himself close in a hug.

"… and I mean, 'can't-live-without-you, my-gut-aches-when-I-think-about-you; love' has no boundaries. Your soul, your heart and your mind are extraordinary and powerful and you will find out true love transcends gender. Gender is an earthly trait that carries no relevance after you evolve. If you find true love, true, true love, let it flourish in your heart, mind and soul. Let it well and over flow touching everyone you meet and come in contact with. If you find that love with a person of the same sex, cherish it, share it, and nurture it. Governments, churches should not dictate who you can love. Everyone should follow their heart and find love, feel love, then share it with everyone. It also needs to be within the human spirit so there can be a mutual exchange; a shared growth; no teddy bears or classic cars."

"Have you shared that with gay people?"

"Many times: but you all should be less concerned about judging same sex marriages or race and more concerned about all the broken hearts in the world who are screaming out for love. Back off gay people who have found love and stop being dicks when two adult, same sex, couples want to adopt a child. Instead of complaining about what two people in love look like anatomically, maybe you all should reach to people who have no one and bring them into your hearts."

140

He slows his walk to make his point. Oh shit. I'm starting to know when he is about to do something.

"Would you like to feel love?"

"I thought I did with my wife last night."

He keeps rolling. It was a rhetorical question for effect making his point.

"Donate your time somewhere helping out people in need. And I don't mean dropping off a couple cans of the shitty, lima beans, you bought by accident that you were never going to eat anyway to a food drive."

"Find someone who has thought that dying is a better solution than another night in the frigid cold. Did you know that when you freeze to death you think you are warming up and getting comfortable? You fall asleep and die. That is why you see homeless people walking in the middle of a cold night. Find that person, look into their eyes after you extend to them a blanket or a warm room, and you will look into their hearts, you will reach into their souls. There you will find love screaming out looking for a place to land. And that place that they land will be your heart. You will find the emptiness of loneliness looking, aching for someone to fill their hearts with joy and that person IS you."

My God has now totally stopped walking and I can tell he is getting extremely upset.

"Would you like to feel love?"

He amps his voice up to a higher pitch. He looks at me. Is he inviting me to feel love or is he talking generally to the passing crowd?

"Find a child who is abused, beaten and tortured and hug them and feel the wealth of unused love swell from their souls into yours. It will flow out of every pour of their little bodies. It will take your breath away. Look into their eyes and see the generous and unconditional love that they wear on their sleeve that gets stripped from them when they are beaten daily, and for no, NO FUCKING reason. Rest your head next to theirs on a tear and blood soaked pillow. Hold them close as they hope to dream about wishes they

141

see on television: hot food, a warm jacket, shoes, or a day without being beaten. Wishes they know will only come true in their dreams."

He is now at the top of his lungs. Initially he sounded out of his mind as rage consumed him. But people passing stop being alarmed and start to listen what he was saying. A crowd assembles around him. They are reaching toward him. He presses on.

"WOULD YOU LIKE TO FEEL LOVE? Find an elderly person living alone, who has to choose between eating or purchasing their medicine. They purchase neither to pay their heating bill. They live off bouillon cubes and warm water. Help them and you will feel love."

"Would you like to feel love? Find a battered wife, sleeping on the floor, next to her bed, without a pillow or blanket, a fist full of her hair torn from her scalp. She lay crying, not for the pain, she's become used to that, but worried how she is going to explain to the people at her work where the large chuck of hair went and why are her eyes are black and blue. They know and say nothing because it embarrasses her. Protect her and you will feel love!"

The crowd increases in size. There are now some thirty or so people standing listening to God, trying to get close enough to touch him.

"Would you like to feel love? Find the middle aged man…"

God looks right at me then points at me. Oh fuck! Knew it. Shit!

"….whose wife was taken by cancer and has lost all will to live. Go find him and…"

The people in the crowd turn their attention to me. I blurt out.

"That's not fair!"

"…. and ask him"

"God Damn you!"

142

He now is wagging his finger at me. People draw nearer to me. They are all coming over to me.

"...and ask him; would you like to feel love? Do you want to feel true love again?"

I mumble.

"Fucker. You are an asshole. Any fucking god wouldn't do this in front of these people...you prick! "

I slump to one knee, my head begins to spin. Tears fill my eyes. I bring my right hand to cover my face. I feel hands all over my back. Visions of my wife taking her last breath cut through me. Shards of broken glass tear open freshly scabbed wounds. I am watching her being buried. I hear her screaming my name from underground!

"Baby!"

God walks up to me. I'm now kneeling on the sidewalk, my left arm stops me from falling flat on my face. I am in the vomiting-over-a-toilet position and feel I could. He reaches under my arm pits and lifts me up; easily. We are eye to eye. I try to draw away. I struggle to free myself from his grasp. I'm sad and pissed.

"Let me go! I thought you were here to help me!"

He stares into my, tear filled eyes.

"Let me go you mother fucker!"

I look into his eyes. They are warm and loving. I want to strangle him! He smiles. He bear hugs me. And I mean a bear hug that lifts me off my heels and I am balancing on my toes.

A huge force of energy; a defibrillator of warmth seizes my senses, every sense. Passion, love rush into my chest and through every bone in my body. I gasp with joy and exhilaration. It is pure ecstasy. I feel as if I am floating off the ground;

weightless. I squeal and laugh loudly. My God pulls me closer to him. He squeezes me so tight he cracks my vertebra as a chiropractor does when he adjusts your back. He whispers.

"Love is all around you. Love is in you. You are love."

The bliss intensifies. My entire body is convulsing, orgasming; continually. There is nothing left to hold on to, to protect. I feel my soul expanding beyond my earthy flesh. Flashes of everything thing I love, once loved and will love again; yes she was there, all Ferris wheeling around my consciousness. I saw my mom; I kiss her, my dad; both dead, friends I haven't seen in decades, my favorite colors, foods, tastes, smells, music, places and images. I'm talking to Mickey Mantle my boyhood hero. My exhalations of love swell from my body and I feel myself giving back the love. There is a pulse to the experience. I am exhaling as the universe inhales. I feel love rush into my body and out, but not just through my lungs; it was bursting through every pour of my body. I see visions of many people celebrating, laughing and having a wonderful time. I am unaware of my surrounding. I am experiencing people now beyond my circle of friends and acquaintances I have gathered on earth thus far. I feel the love of hundreds then thousands of people. I am now weightless vapor of energy, the euphoria increases. I am not immersed in euphoria; I am euphoria. This is love. This is active, unbridled, powerful, unconditional love.

God softens his hug, the experience ratchets back as quick as it was given to me. I fall back into a loose embrace. He needs to support me. He holds me with both hands by the back of my shirt. I begin to gain my legs and start reacquainting myself with my surroundings. But there is something else. I can hardly move and I can't speak. I feel hands on my back. I draw myself toward God and work hard to rotate my upper body to find four people I have never met resting their hand on my back and shoulders. Four total strangers: a child around six, two women, one elderly man; all with their open hand on my back. And more people had their hands on the four people's back.

"They empowered you. I empowered you. You empowered you. Could you feel it, the accelerated joy, and the exhilarating power of love? How do you feel now?"

I am having trouble speaking. Did I have a stroke? Was I in a state frozen animation? Feeling is returning to my mouth, tongue, my heart; racing. My hair is on end, smells of smoke and the fillings in my mouth sizzle when my tongue touches them. I am shaking. My cotton mouth begins to find some spit. It tastes like sulfur. Blood runs from my left nostril and I am soaking wet from my shoulder to my knees, but only in the front where I was touched by God's hug. Did I piss myself?

21

"I went there one Sunday and told them I was God.
They gave me water, five dollars, a pamphlet on drug addiction
and escorted me out."

"How do you feel?"

How do I feel, I can barely move. But past the funkiness
I find myself with this feeling of strength, power, a full night's
sleep; contentment. My mouth still is not back to whatever
normal is. Stuttering.

"Gr.. gr... gr... great. "

"You say something Tony the Tiger?"

I piss myself and God's got jokes.

"Do you feel AWESOME!?"

I nod my head. Yes.

" *Happy?"*

Nod again.

"Loved?"

Nodding quickly, now like a school boy with a crush, but on whom? I am still in his loose embrace. Six inches now separate our chests. The piss all over me, smells more like sweat. I still struggle to catch my breath. God looks into my eyes…

"That is the power of love and we shared ours with you."

Still struggling to speak.

"and ….. and….mine with th – th - th - them?"

"Yeah: you pulled your weight. Welcome to the future of the universe."

The four people smile and move on. They weren't 'Children of the Corn' creepy, or anything, in fact they seem very normal and very comfortable and went on their separate ways. Were they drawn to me or God?

"They were drawn to you…"

"Th- h - h a –a –a –at's the th-th – th – third ti – ti – ti time you answered a question I was th – th – th - th - thinking and not speaking."

"I was guessing."

I breathe deep, catching my breath trying to calm myself. My speech returns.

"But they were drawn to you, and your 'no-place-for-your-love', 'man-in-deep-pain', 'someone-help-me, YOU! They were drawn to you! They came to love you. That's how it is supposed to work. When someone is in pain people who love covet and share their love to mend, to protect, to repair. We got your love and we gave you ours. How about we take a minute over there?"

God points to a cement bench at a bus stop. There is an awful photo on it of a strange looking man in a priest's collar. Someone had blackened out his front teeth and gave him a pirate's patch over his right eye. The headline next to the creepy photo read: "Visit Pastor Bartimaeus and Find God This Sunday,

147

At First Bethel Church." I point to the bench headline as he helps me sit down.

"Check that out. You are supposed to be at church this Sunday."

"I went there one Sunday and told them I was God. They gave me water, five dollars, a pamphlet on drug addiction and escorted me out. I tried to put the five in the poor box before I left and they told me to take it and buy food instead of drugs or booze. Very thoughtful."

"Enough of all that. Could you please tell me what just happened?"

God positions me on the bench. I have the muscle control of Raggedy Andy.

"Did you dig it? It was very cool and I thought you should have a little taste."

"Taste? Taste of what?"

"I can't say I didn't mean to amp you up and upset you; I did."

"Taste of what?"

"What I wanted to show you I didn't want confused with other happy moments we were sharing. I wanted you pissed, mad and upset."

"Well, you did a good job. Taste....of.....what?"

"It was important that you appreciated the power of pure love, true love from someone else besides your wife and family; the power of the universe. You needed to see how love can be harnessed to help and make people mentally, spiritually and also physically stronger. It is your eventual future. You were crippled by the loss of your wife. You were dying breath by breath. So you need to see and feel what people can do for people. You felt the power of love from someone who can harness the energy and I shared it with you, and man, did you really need it. It is the same energy you shared with your wife when I brought you back to her. Are you happy now?"

"Yes I am. I'm ecstatic."

"That's the power of love baby! When you all evolve imagine being able to share that with one another and eventually large groups of people, then everyone. As you will see some day, love is everything in the universe. Love, energy is the universe. You need to share it and cultivate it regardless of their sex or color and regardless what level mentally you are presently at. You MUST reach out. It is a gift that must be shared by all people regardless of who they find it with. Shame on the people who think they have the right to judge anyone."

I can't get the God damn smile off my face.

"From now on, how about, no more judging of people regardless of color or sexual preference, just don't judge. I don't, not the living or the dead, HA, a prayer reference for you. Why should anyone else? How about instead of judging, take that time and help people to find love, and to mend broken hearts? How's your heart doing now?"

"Much better! Mended or mending I think."

I am mentally exhausted though. I don't know if I can handle anymore monster revelations.

"Would you mind if I ask some questions that are a bit tamer so I don't get soaked with... what is this: piss? Ghostbusters slime?"

"Sure: just Sweat. Did you just say Ghostbusters slime?"

Laughing.

"What's so funny?"

"One was funnier than two."

"Huh? Oh, agreed, but the art curator in two was a stitch. What was his name?"

God is still laughing hysterically, I watch as he lazy Susan's scenes from the movie in his head and acting them out; master of the universe; bad at charades. He flies into this bad German accent and flubs a few lines from the movie curator in the movie.

149

Talk to God

"Dr. Janosz Poha"

More wild, hysterical laughter.

"How did you know that? Is that a God, knows everything trick?"

"I bunked at a shelter a few years back. They had a v.c.r. and three movies. One was broken, the other one was a tape on how to kick drug addiction and the third was Ghostbusters II. Guess which one we put on every night? We knew almost every line"

"Are there Ghosts?"

"You said you were going to ask some tamer questions."

"I thought that would be."

"No problem. Boo! Ha! Books and movies depict ghosts haunting places where they have died, usually violently. This is not true. When a person evolves, or dies using your term, regardless how it happened, and for what reason, their soul, their spirit, begins the amazing evolution and starts to assist in the expansion of the universe. It begins with the feeling you just felt and just gets better. There is no hanging back to take care of unfinished business, or to find your murderer. Your soul does not hold grudges or waits around until all wrongs have been righted. That is just movie making baloney. You evolve immediately to the next evolution. The soul is swept from any earthly attachments. And remember what you feel like when you evolve?"

He points to my soaked from sweat front of my clothing.

"Yeah?"

"Imagine that on a much higher level, plus there is a third thing you do once you evolve."

"You mean I just don't drift around with my wife and friends getting soaked with sweat when I evolve?"

"You also are part in the expanding and growing universe."

"Hold the fuck on, you lost me."

"Maybe that's best at this point. This might be too much for you."

150

"Could you try me? Please."

"No."

God starts walking away from me on the bench. I get up to follow and nearly fall, still rubber legged.

"Hold on! Come on! I can get it. Try me!"

God shrugs his shoulders and lets out a breath in frustration. How fucking hard could this be?

"Okay; but no continuing questions on the subject. First, stop imagining when you evolve you will look like a human being with angel wings, floating around the universe, like religious stories would have you believe. You floating on a cloud, with your wife, looking down at people on earth, scouting for a place to haunt or just being someone's guardian angel is not what happens? No such thing. When you evolve you will evolve into emotional, intellectual and physical energy. An existence you, as a human haven't assumed, guessed, processed or even imagined. Generations from now when you develop your mental capacity here on Earth it will start to dawn on you that your abilities will transcend your earthly coil. You will evolve into a hi-bred of conscious energy. The universe becomes your new place to live: the place where you inhabit. It grows with you and your energy feeds the growth of the universe."

"What?"

"Figures. You must remember, humans are made up of atoms; energy. That energy of all human life began from one living cell and every living thing has evolved from the first living cell and that journey continues. When you evolve; the energy evolves with you. And your energy grows exponentially when you are evolving because of the love and support of the souls you know as friends and relations."

"How much energy do I have now?"

"You have enough energy to make your heart beat. You know: the mystery of life. It makes your ticker tick."

"So after I die I become a fireball of loving energy out in front of the expanding universe leading the way? And the more love I share on earth the bigger the amassed energy?"

151

"You are not a fireball. You are energy, thinking with the ability to deduce, love, you remember catching up with the missus. As far as leading the way as the universe expands, let's just say for the time being, you are part of the big, group push from the middle."

"I think I got it."

God shoots me a look like he knows I don't have it but is letting me off the hook. I want to walk a bit. The afternoon breeze was drying my clothing and I was getting a chill. God supports my left side by scooping his shoulder under my shoulder. In a matter of feet I have found my legs. We part and pick up the pace.

"I'm bummed about no ghosts, just us evolving into energy?"

"You have a way of sounding sarcastic and ignorant all in the same breath. I tell you the secret of the universe and what happens after you DIE …"

"I thought it is evolved…"

"It is! I am making a point. You are not mentally ready. But you are acting and sounding your age as a developing human. You are still infants. You are bummed there are no ghosts."

"That wasn't what I was going for. I just have trouble with getting my arms around it."

"I know. You may never be able to for at least a couple million years. But, we tried. I promise you though; you are all getting a lot smarter."

"Really?"

"Really. I will show you in a few blocks but appreciate this: your grasp of the truth of how things really are and the history and answers to how they occurred are now within reach. In fact, since I would say…. since about 1980 everything written prior to that was garbage and guessing. You are beginning to see the reality of the universe. Yes, as far off on the horizon it may be, there is a little bit coming into view. It will be a good time for me. I won't get my ass kicked so frequently or killed so quickly."

152

"But no ghosts?"

God shoots me a 'just fucking with me now' look and smiles.

"No ghosts like you were hoping. It's just impossible. But there is contact with people who have passed with their spirit and souls as they evolve. I mentioned earlier that when humans eventually get the use of your entire brain, probably in fifty million years or so, you will be able to stay in contact and support and love the person as they evolve into their next evolution and beyond. The process of evolving...."

"Right."

"When you start using your entire brain, you will celebrate the process you call death, similarly as you celebrate a person's wedding, all loved ones will be part of it. It will be an exchange of love back and forth. Those evolving can reach back like we did with your wife and visa-vie."

I began to get cold as my sweat soaked clothes began to dry in afternoon breeze.

"Today there are unique occasions when a human, either through a genetic flaw or they got hit by lightning or something, but a portion of their brains are advanced and they have the ability to communicate with evolving people like you all will be able to do in the future. Today in your society you refer to these people as psychic, or clairvoyant, but someday all people will be 'psychic, clairvoyant' as you put it. And everyone will be able to see, as you put it; 'ghosts'."

"So if someone can talk to dead or sorry, evolved people."

"Evolving or evolved."

"Okay, if someone presently can communicate with people who have 'evolved', they possess some of the brain power that we will all have in a few thousand years."

"More like millions of years."

153

"Really? Can you teach it to me ...now?"

"You don't have the skill package. It's like asking me if you could fly. Sure, I could tell you to run into the wind, flap your arms, and jump off a cliff, but you do not have the physical capabilities to get off the ground. You are a human not a bird. Same thing with your brain today; you physically and especially mentally are not capable to communicate with the spirit and soul while evolving, or after it has evolved at this time."

"Nothing now?"

"Now, you will, once in a great while, get an echo. You will be dreaming at night, your mind; wide open, usually under extreme duress or stress, accelerating and accepting and your undying love for one another will be directed right at each other at the exact same moment. You will wake up feeling like you spent time with, in your case, her, but as of today, in your present evolutionary state, you can't communicate on your own; a stereo without speakers."

"I have seen movies, read books where someone who dies for a few minutes then returns to life, speaks of seeing a bright light they were drawn to. They also say they see their lives flash in front of their eyes and see dead loved ones. Is that true?"

"Kind of: they can't see a light, they can't see anything. Their physical bodies are shutting down or have shut down, so seeing is not really happening. They are beginning the evolutionary process, but I know that process doesn't have a light. Their soul and spirit are being drawn to their place in the next evolution of life, evolving into the energy of the expanding universe. They are being led by their spirit and soul's natural instinct, and by people they love, and who love them."

"Their life is not flashing in front of their 'eyes,' they are being touched by people who love them, so they assume they are seeing a quick history of their earthly lives."

"They are not?"

"Nope. When a person is evolving their love reaches out to all their loved ones evolved or human. The support is given to ease the confusion of the transition. Remember at the moment your soul leaves your physical body, this gift, the ability to share and grow in love, is thrust upon you. So there is an adjustment period. This is important SO share this with everyone you meet. The love you take is equal to the love you make."

"Cut the shit; that's a Beatles quote from Abby Road; right?"

"Right, but actually that's a Shakespearean couplet. Paul borrowed it and tweaked it. I told Paul about the line. I shared it with him he added it in. It was our last cut on our last album. Paul wanted something catchy and emotional and he knew how important the message was to me. I had been sharing with him my beliefs regarding the afterlife. I can't tell you how many times when we were younger, and closer, I almost told him. I don't think he would have believed me. He was very into himself. And if I would have told him, I'm God, I would have totally blown the chemistry of the group."

"Yeah, so God got first crack at the groupie chicks?"

"Funny. Let me get back to how it works. The more people you love and share love with on earth, and I just don't mean the opposite sex: it includes friends, even strangers, all the people who you shared love with, these souls, evolved or still on earth, are now becoming part of you through your evolution. You are evolving into the energy and the expansion of the universe together in unison. Plus they bring the love and support and power of their loved ones: a Facebook of love for the evolving soul. It is the power that fuels the universe."

"Okay, but what about being drawn into the 'bright light thing'...."

I do the quotes thing with my fingers.

"... people talk about; like you are being called to cross over to heaven like in Poltergeist?"

"Well as I mentioned, you are not seeing anything out of your eyes. But when a soul, your spirit, is evolving it is also guiding you but no light. These assumptions are just guesses, stories by humans. And most of these guesses came from religious leaders who want to frame heaven in their perception and to keep everyone believing that you must be good or you won't go to the bright shiny place called heaven. And if you are not good you will end up in the scary darkness or worse, HELL!"

"Is there a....?"

"Hold on. Let me finish. Your present knowledge of the evolution of your souls paints death as dark and lonely. Not at all; it is the greatest moment in your lives and the process is on auto pilot. You have no choices and the quality of the moment is based on how many people you share love with throughout your life's journey. Imagine the few

moments we spent over there with four people sharing love. Now imagine a few thousand people joining you. The feeling is indescribable, the energy is massive. And that energy drives your soul and spirit. When someone evolves, they never want to come back, ever. Light? No light, just love."

"I never thought love was so important."

"Love: those natural feelings you have, that draw you to one another, is also the same power that drives the universe. It's just hard for you to comprehend. You think of love as deep caring, romance, Valentine's Day, the bond you have with your wife or between one another. True, yes, but that is such a small part of the weight and velocity of love's power and it's the only part you presently can understand. But it is so hard for you to comprehend, to process in your present mental state."

"Love?"

"Love is the building block that drive the universe and presently it is in a child's hands who doesn't understand it yet."

"We're the children?"

"Right now you are."

"Can I ask the question now?"

"Sure, an easy one."

"Is…. Is there a hell?"

> God hesitates… looks to the right, then to the left. I lurch forward and crane my neck toward him. A large smile stretches his lips, a sun blister oozes some blood and clear liquid. He waits. He knows I am dying to know; where does God store the bad guys?

"Nope! No hell. No such place."

"I am a loving God and I don't punish anyone, plus I can't. Remember I said earth and humans are on auto pilot? The gifts I have given you were delivered through your

evolution and not a judgment day thing. Again, I don't have the time or the desire to send someone to a hell."

"You don't flood the earth when there are too many sinners?"

"No. I am not watching. I will tell you this. The strength, and the power of love you will possess, as mentioned before, is increased by the quantity of people you have shared love. The more people, the more love. The more love, the more energy you are, the bigger part you play in the expanding universe."

"But that means….."

Interrupting.

"Ah, look who's catching up?"

"…that means if you were a hateful person and did not love and share love, you will have limited energy in the next evolution and you will be void of love or energy. You will be alone won't you?"

"I guess you could put it that way"

"Not just alone; powerless. When everyone else is out there evolving and growing the universe that person who has pushed away love and does not enfold themselves in love are destined to continue an existence void of love beyond their evolution because love is energy. No energy, no fun. So a soul with limited energy never feels a part of the larger universal expansion."

"Well, that's about right and, the reason love is so important. And if you treat humans poorly, there would not just be a void of a connection with that person, but a negative energy that exhausts the soul of the person who treated people poorly. So if eternal loneliness is hell, I guess there is a hell."

God stops in his tracks, which is fine with me. My feet were beginning to really ache. We must have walked no less than 30 miles from my office since Friday night.

22

*We are children, no, worse: we are child bullies
in a world that requires unconditional love. Fuck.*

"Why are we stopping?"

"We're here?"

"We're where?"

"We're here…..."

I take the moment to slip off my shoe to offer my right
foot a pain free moment.

*"We are at the place….the place where my miracles, the miracles of the universe have
been recorded for all humans to share and learn from. Many of my greatest creations are
captured in illustrations, books, verse and sonnet. We are at THE place where the true
disciples and their teachings have been etched in history!"*

I hopped and spun on my shoed foot, circling the entire
area.

"What are you talking about?"

I see no church, no synagogue, mosque, temple, cathedral, mission, shrine; nothing, but it dawns on me that we are standing at the front on the main branch of the public library.

I hop scotch around again, this time straining my eyes searching for a church maybe somewhere further down, a steeple or bell tower. Nothing! His enthusiasm charges my expectations. I must have missed it. God jumps up on the ledge of a large fountain. He lifts his voice higher. People begin to stop.

"All who can hear my voice gather and be educated and enriched with the love of God."

"At the library? What the fuck are you doing?"

He doesn't miss a beat and ignores me.

"We stand on holy ground; draw close and learn; for this is the place where the story of God and my miracles are preserved for all humans to learn, evolve, and enjoy. These are the teaching of life and my love."

People start to gather. He is sounding like a homeless lunatic. You don't notice when you are talking to him one on one, but when he grand stands, you can just see marbles falling out of his head. But, he stands proud, straightens his jacket, combs his hair off his forehead with his hand, throws out his chest, proud of his appearance, and waits for anyone to stop and listen. More stop to listen or be entertained by a loon. He repeats his invitation even louder.

"We stand on holy ground; draw close and learn; for this is the place where the story of God and my miracles are preserved…. (interrupted)"

God got someone's attention. A black and white squad car pulls up, onto the sidewalk with the blue and red lights flashing, stops 10 feet from God and the fountain. It must be cool to be able to pull up on a sidewalk or anywhere you are not supposed to drive; a perk for the men in blue. I watch as two officers slowly get out of the car. I wonder why they always move slow exiting their car. I guess no one likes to rush into danger.

My first reaction is to fall back, blend into the assembling crowd. It dawns on me that a bigger crowd quickly gathers when the police with the car on the sidewalk, the city's muscle, still cool, roll up with flashing lights and sirens. From television when people see police they think; possible violence, a shoot-out, but for sure some undignified, public humiliation. Why is that? Why do people rush to witness pain, violence but never rush to extend love to one another? We are truly the infants God thinks we are.

The area is getting clogged with people now. They seem to be crawling out of the wood work to get what I thought was a close look at the officers and the squad on the sidewalk. What is odd to me is they aren't curious as I was by the police, but more intrigued with God. They seem all very concerned about my homeless friend all of a sudden. A handful draw behind him, so close that the officers had to ask people to back up.

My God explains to the police officers why he is speaking in such a loud voice. There is my God, hair and face a dirty mess, clothes rancid with sweat, fecal matter, dried food, missing his left finger, a boot with no tongue on one foot, a woman's gym shoe on the other, punctured lung, scars and a look of pride, dignity and most of all love in his eyes, on his lips, across his face. His expression looks so out of place looking at his clothes.

Is my God just a nut? No! God, how many times have you stood there and have been persecuted? How many times have they not listened? How many times have you been crucified? You are right, we are not ready for you; not now. You are still too early. We are children, no, worse: we are child bullies in a world that requires unconditional love. Fuck.

"He's with me!"

The entire area surrounding the fountain freezes and everyone turns to find the voice in the crowd. I repeat myself.

"He's with me! Sorry I am late."

I try my hand at acting. I help God down from his perch. I turn my attention to the stunned police officers.

" I had to…park the car. Sorry, he gets that way sometimes."

To God's surprise I try to quickly escort him away from the area. I am stopped by one of the officer's pressing his night stick across my chest blocking my path.

"Hold on, where's your shoe?"

"My what?"

"Your shoe; you are missing a shoe."

Fuck. I can't believe it. In the heat of the moment I forgot to put my fucking shoe back on.

"And what did you lay down in? Why are your clothes stained with, what is that smelly funk, on the front of your clothes?"

What am I supposed to say. It is universal love; and no shoe?

"Why don't you boys go stand over there?"

The cop points to the fountain edge near where God was standing and preaching.

"Face the fountain, spread your legs and place you hands apart on the ledge."

God and I follow his direction. We are shoulder to shoulder leaning down against the two foot high fountain ledge where people would typically sit. I am totally nervous and scared. I have never been in trouble or ever had to speak to the police much less stand spread eagle. I notice if I crane my shoulders and neck I can see my reflection in the pool of water, in the base of the fountain. I look totally like shit. God sees me leaning and looking in and does the same. Now I can see both of our reflections in the fountain water. Pennies lying in the bottom of the fountain pool dot our reflection. Oddly, at first glance I look so shitty and he looks just like he did when I met him, and to my surprise, we look like we were in about the same shape except for our expressions. I look scared as shit and he is glowing with a Christmas morning smile.

A firm, large hand grabs the top of my head, then slides down my spine, now two hands around, through and in between my legs and genitals. I am being patted down! Oh my fucking God, I am being patted down. I can't deal with it. I'm not a criminal. Can my life get any worse? Every time I think I am holding it together it all unravels. What the fuck am I doing here? I begin to snivel a bit, eyes well with tears. God slides his hand over a few inches and grabs my hand and holds it tight as my public embarrassment finishes and his begins. His strength rushes through my hand, up my arm and throughout my body. It was a jolt of fortitude. The guy sure has fucking game.

"You boys got anything in your pockets? What this?"

The officer reaches in God's right jacket pocket and pulls out, my now cold and gooey wad of hamburger and fries and flings them on the sidewalk. A look of sadness crosses God's face. I whisper:

"I can buy you a new one later."

He smiles. The cop announces to his partner that "we are clean", a metaphor for not having any weapons or drugs in our possession. Actually that literally is the furthest thing from the truth. I haven't showered in two days now and only God knows how long it's been since he has last showered. Funny: "only He knows." The police wander back to their squad car to probably tell their dispatcher that we are not a threat or that they don't require back-up. God looks at me and smiles warmly. He subtlety swings his head around side to side to get a bead on the police and what they are doing. They have all but forgotten about us. God turns back to me.

162

He reaches down and scoops up a handful of water from the fountain and cups the water to my forehead. The coolness actually feels really good right then. The water splashes through his fingers and onto my face. He looks deep into my eyes.

"Your heart has been scarred but not broken. Find the love you need from me and from all others. Share in their love, give them yours. Your heart will mend with the love from your wife, your family and friends. But more importantly open your heart to strangers. Reach for them and they will reach back for you."

God stares deeply into my eyes.

"The strength and love of God and the love of the entire universe are now a part of you. Go and share it with those in need."

God and I separate. Swaying back and forth, I steady myself, placing my left hand on the ledge of the fountain. I am thrust back to the reality of the moment. I pull my shirt tail out and wipe my face. I feel a hand slide off my back. What? But my God is in front of me. Curious, I look back to find a woman kneeling behind me with her hand on my shoulder. I smile and she smiles back. I stand to find a teenager behind her kneeling with his hand on her shoulder. Behind him an old man, behind him his wife, her wheel chair lying on its side, next to her, behind her a security guard, behind him another man, then another woman and on and on. I stop counting the conga love line of people at twenty four. It seems that every person in the park was part of the line. I think these people are gravitating to the fountain because of the police action but as I am noticing they came because of God. They were drawn to, to, to him! Everyone here was sharing God's love. It is contagious. Cars have stopped and are abandoned, doors open, engines running right in the middle of the street, drawn to join. It is an amazing moment and I am the center of it.

Slowly the line breaks up. Warm smiles are exchanged and people go on their way. A dozen or so people circle the fountain, kneel over the edge of the ledge and calmly were waiting. What are they waiting for? Then it dawns on me. They want God to bless them; maybe baptize them like he just did me? Methodically he walks to every person, leans down and scoops up some water from the fountain, places it on their foreheads whispering:

"The strength and love of God and the love of the entire universe are now a part of you. Go and share it with those in need."

People who were leaving circle back and take a position at the ledge of the fountain.

God spends time with everyone. He offers words of encouragement and direction to men, children, women of all races and income levels; everyone. There was no preferential treatment for anyone. It was a true love affair with everyone. People try to give him, shoes, money, clothing food and he warmly declines all offerings. When someone begins to cry speaking with God, usually while sharing a story of a loved one's passing, a handful of people would gravitate to them and place their hand on their back, shoulder or head. God would always press his hand to their hearts; I think it was a metaphor for fixing the break, but what the fuck do I know.

Everyone gathers around him. They listen intently to his every word. They do not question who he is, they know. Plus the joy of them knowing that there is an eternity and that eternity includes their loved ones is like watching true joy animated in Technicolor. Old people very late in their years, are relieved and especially euphoric. While God is baptizing, I guess it is baptizing, I go looking for my shoe. Over an hour passes, as he finally finishes with the last person, God glances my way, he waves me over.

"Are you ready?"

"Ready for what? You said you wanted to go to one of your favorite places. I assumed the fountain was it. This isn't the holy ground you were talking about?"

"This is a fountain. How can a fountain be the place where my story, the story of God and my miracles are preserved? It's over there."

He nods in the direction behind me. I thought I scanned the area pretty well for a church. Emotionally strained and physically exhausted, I roll my head around to find...... the public library?

"You want to go to the library? All your miracles are in the public library?"

"Yep and its 4:00 p.m. and it closes at eight on Saturdays so we have very little time."

He sees that I am surprised.

"You thought it would be a church or something? I saw you looking. Those guys don't get it, they are in the church business, I am in the love business. But I understand how you could assume such a thing. You were raised with the stories. You knew no different."

"For the record, this is the first time I ever want to go to the library."

"That's funny. Let's go read...."

".... about your miracles?"

"Yes!"

We start across the street. Well, not a street with traffic, it was more of a service street separating the park and fountain from the library. You couldn't drive on it with your car unless you were a police officer. I still dig the cop car thing. Now that I look at the fountain, park and library, I am sure the architects, city planners, and landscape designers imagined going into the library, checking out a book or two, and then spending a leisurely afternoon in the park, by the fountain, reading Dickens. I am sure they didn't imagine the drug trade and don't forget the improv baptisms. Some park.

We made our way up the five steps to a wonderful architectural facade that looks like it was directly lifted from Fillippo Brunelleschi, who built the Cathedral of Florence in the

165

Renaissance period. The building places emphasis on symmetry, proportion, geometry, and demonstrates in the architecture of classic antiquity, in particular ancient Roman architecture. It gives the building a look of stately security, but also brought the building to life and what God doesn't care to notice it also looks a lot like a church and it looks out of place against the depressing canvas of urban decay.

What is also blatantly noticeable about the building was the shitty black spray paint of gang signs, virtually unintelligible due to turf war paint overs. The building is a metaphorical social, pendulum with a treasure trove of knowledge on the inside and the void of any common sense and total lack of knowledge on the outside.

Some really heavy, old doors; they had to be nine feet tall and weigh a couple hundred pounds each, set under a wonderful hemispherical dome foyer with another set of less attractive steel doors on the opposite side of the dome protect the inside from the outside. I had to actually lean on the door to get it to swing. Once propped with my shoulder, I wave God in ahead of me. As he was moving through the doorway and into the foyer, I glance back, across the street, at the fountain. There had to be a hundred people just standing there watching him enter the library.

This is truly a weird ass weekend.

23

They brainwash the masses with horrible stories
about God and my wrath.
I don't have any wrath.

He walks through the main hall, turns right after about
50 feet, and heads up stairs. You could tell by his pace and lack of
hesitation he knows where he was going. I was thinking: This is
the main branch of the library and as an educated man, I felt a
little embarrassed for never, ever, visiting this library or any
branch of the library - though I have been living in his town for
over 20 years.

We take the stairs two steps per gallop, clump-clop,
clump-clop, woman's gym shoe then army boot, gym shoe then
army boot. There is a yellowed, sun-faded poster taped to the
green, ceramic tiled wall, at the top of the stairwell, corners
tattered. It shows a mother reading a book to her young child
enfolded in her arms. The simple, three-word, headline: READ.
TEACH. LOVE. Without breaking his gait, God smacks the
poster, calling my attention to it, shoots me a wink and a nod so I
am sure to get it and continues around the corner.

"That's what it is all about."

We are speed walking now, childlike, I expect to be firmly scolded by a librarian to slow down! I hurry to keep pace with him. Walking abreast, we approach the main intersection of the second level. A large terrazzo tile design on the floor depicting the earth, a true, unappreciated, work of art that people walk over, marks the cross roads of all accumulated human knowledge and information. A sign hangs from above the earthly floor art, directing visitors to REFERENCE and ART AND LITERATURE to the right, FICTION and PERIODICALS to the left. Just off to the right, sitting in a fancy, wooden, book cradle, and illuminated from above, was the largest book in the library: the Bible. It has to weigh 50 pounds if not more. I fire a quick glance at God. He whispers;

"Fiction."

"Serious?"

He then stops dead in his tracks.

"The Bible? I brought you here to learn the truth."

I stop.

"So the Bible has no truth in it?"

"If the word love is in it, there is some truth in it. Beyond that it's mostly fish wrapping. Now, if you are extremely religious, you believe the Bible is a realistic historical document that should be followed to the letter, and that you should adapt your daily life to its teaching. If you are little closer to curious, you may believe the Bible is framed as allegory, you are typically educated, tripping on agnostic, and find it easier to say at parties that you believe in a 'supreme being,' but are not sure about all that mumbo-jumbo. That perception is actually the beginning of your mental development to get beyond the Bible and religion and start getting to the real truth."

God glances around for a place to sit. He settles on leaning against the end of a tall bookshelf across from the Bible. I find a similar place one aisle over. We are both leaning our shoulders against the ends of book shelves at the entrance of an aisle, facing each other. Five feet of worn, industrial-gray carpet

separates us. Who buys that carpet? It must have looked old when
it was installed. You can smell the age in the rug. Something has
caught God's attention in his pants. As he makes adjustments, and
I'm hoping he is not about to pea where he is standing, I draw
inward to try to wrap my mind around the last 24 hours, and I just
can't.

Oddly, operating way outside my nature, I am gripped
with some sort of James Dean, *Rebel Without a Cause*, laissez faire
attitude where it feels better to not care how I think, or care about
what I do. Freedom? I used to wrap myself in mourning, and
before that pity, and before that a victim's coma of personal
destruction. But now I feel that being here is right, going forward
is right, and listening to God is right. As twisted as all this must
seem right now, it feels right and I want to know more. God
jumps right in.

"Let me start by saying human kind doesn't need rule books."

I fire back sharply.

"When you say 'rule book' you are referring to the Bible?"

Without speaking, God nods, yes.

*"The love you are born with, given to you from your mother, the love, or energy that drives
the universe, that is to be shared with one another; that you have in your soul, your spirit,
your heart, your mind...is enough to guide you. That being said, I also don't mind, in fact
I was hoping humankind, groups, tribes, communities, sharing this knowledge, would
build entire nations around the simple message of love and celebrate it frequently in some
form. And even if it weren't embraced like I hoped, I thought individuals would share it
by speaking or writing books, something so simple, or in today's world, sending a
computer file in an email. Let it be known when I spoke about creating and sharing a
common message about love that it should pass from generation to generation..."*

"Like religion."

*"Yes, I am not against religion or any group gathering to share the teachings of love, but
what happened..."*

169

Talk to God

Here it comes.

"… is that they ALWAYS got it wrong?"

He points to the Bible.

"It's when they stray from these natural impulses of a mom's love and interject their own agenda-usually control, tyranny, dictatorship - and totally screw things up. This is how wars, revolts, or revolutions all have begun. When the guys in charge of religions start dictating unnatural edicts, like persecution, slavery, or believing they are in some way superior to other people, folks will ultimately not put up with them, and the next thing you know everybody is swinging at each other."

He's preaching to me. He is on a roll.

"How loving and Godly is this religion you have now if they are warring?"

"Warring?"

"For 200 years and that wasn't the first time, starting around 1095 ACE, the Christians were fighting the Muslims to take back Jerusalem. Two hundred years! Is that getting any better over there? I didn't think so. Another: in 1506 Pope Julius led, as in like on a horse with a sword, led armies against Piragua and Bologna - the frickin' pope! What in heaven's name do these people have anything to do with love and my message? They are fighting in wars! They are not in the love business, they are in the ego 'I'm in charge,' fear and guilt business. And here is what really pisses me off: when some numbnuts, kills someone or some group of people in the name of God! How dare they? They are on my intergalactic shit list. It is the only time I wish I had the powers people think I do. You would see my wrath then. Go ahead and raise your hand against another human in the name of God!"

"That's pretty loud for a library."

"Sorry but for the love of Christ."

That shit sounds so odd coming out of his mouth.

"So the Bible threatens while promoting fear and guilt?"

"... and a bunch of other things, especially the notion - and this runs through both Testaments - that if you are bad, I will be mad at you and you can't go to heaven. The other is the only way you get to 'heaven' is through professing your faith, telling me you sinned and being sorry. If you don't, you can't come in. That is just not true!"

God amps up again.

"The Old Testament is the worst of the two but not by much. The New Testament has much more of me and my message in it, but it is still a mess riddled with 'be good for goodness sake'... or else bullshit. But the Old Testament is filled with lies, fear, guilt, and death. And who is in charge of all that? Well, according to that book over there; I was. The Bible is supposed to be the book of truth or the book of God; my lessons. For your information, I didn't write it nor did I ask anyone else to write it."

"But most people believe in the Bible as the true teachings of You, God."

"I know. They are all wrong. My message, if I would have sent down a message, which I wouldn't have, and didn't, is only about love and sharing love with each other, a love you will all find inside you. And the cool thing about love is the energy of the expanding universe. Why would you not want to love?"

He bangs his forehead on the wooden façade of the shelf, smiling at me, looking for my approval of his pale attempt at comedy.

"Both testaments were written with the pretense that there is a supreme being: me, somewhere up in the sky with a big scoreboard determining if you are going to heaven or hell. It just isn't true. I built the place, gave you all free will, 'free will'-"

God does the quote fingers. He likes quote fingers.

"- and the power of love. Free will and the love you share are what grows the universe and grows the quality and strength of your existence beyond your evolution. That's it. Also I do not govern your existence or offer guidance. Any lesson I may have wanted to share is in your nature or what I am telling you now. I am you. You all are me. We are all attached, and part of the universe, through the energy of what you call love."

"How did it all the books get so screwed up?"

"No book like that should exist or should have been written, but free will swings both ways. In the not-too-distant future, you will dismiss these stories and that book - once you develop your minds. You will understand more and that will open your hearts. But explain that to the church or the people who wrote that book -"

He points again to the fifty pound bible.

"-and they will fight to the death to protect the lies. Most of the religious people who hatched the stories in that book and passed them down generation to generation are still the ones running religion today and are usually the furthest from being Godly. Godly includes humility and unconditional love. Trust me when I tell you, the high priests are rarely humble or without conditions. The fact that they live the charade and suppress their followers is a big step backward to where you are trying to get to. They brainwash the masses with horrible stories about God and My wrath. I just don't have any wrath."

24

On the seventh day I rested was also a whopper.
It was written that way to make sure people showed up for church
instead of boozing and ass grabbing.

"Wrath? For instance"

"Want a quick crash course on the Old Testament?"

"Do I have a choice?"

"Nope; I'll make it quick and highlight some of the stories that drive me nutty."

God leans his head back, cracks his neck by swiveling his head counter-clockwise, and draws in a deep breath. I can tell He hates to speak of this but I think He believes it is important for me to hear.

"To begin with, when God spoke in the Old Testament, according to The Book, he was speaking to people on earth from the sky, the heavens, heaven, in a loud, made for television, movie-announcers, booming voice. But that wouldn't have been so bad, except what they said I was saying from the sky. That was pretty horrible stuff."

"I thought the Old Testament was all about the creation of the world?"

"That's the first chapter, the book of Genesis, and that is also a load of crap, but it was a great story; real science fiction. My guess is they must have been just guessing AND referencing some of the information I gave to them. But in their defense, the people creating the stories were not rocket scientists; these were pretty simple people."

"What society has proven over the years is that a community functions better with the knowledge of a supreme being. The problem is I don't know if I have helped over the years trying to explain my true message when I visited. The by-product of my visits is the Bible, but they just couldn't leave the message simple like I told it to them, they had to add the crap to it. But I still believe that if I didn't steer some of the information, I could only imagine you would still be worshiping the sun."

"Alright, let's not cry over spilled false gods. Let's hear about the Old Testament and where they went off message. Commonsense tells us that the Earth and the universe took a lot longer than six days to create."

"Yes and no. Yes regarding the earth, no on the universe. But that is not as farfetched as when I was supposed to have done it. According to the Old Testament and actual religious fanatics today, that believe the universe was created by Me 5950 years ago."

I smile because what I have learned about my God in the short time we have been together is that he has a bit of a devilish sense of humor, and I know from my seventh grade biology class things are a lot older than 6,000 years.

"It wasn't, was it?"

"No. Those biblical authors were off by a few years. The universe is 10.6 billion years old. Today's scientists, geologists and astronomers have it pegged it at 13.7 billion years, but they will get smarter and the technology will get better for making these determinations, and they will eventually land the age of this universe at 14.2 billion. But for sure it isn't only 6,000. Want some simple proof?"

"Sure, but did You say 'this universe'?"

"I did, but stay with me. There are plenty of things that are going to be startling in the next few hours, so let's try to take them in common sense order. Let's get back to the idea that religion postulates that the earth is 6,000 years old."

"Fine."

"If you go outside and pick up any rock in the park across the street and take it to a geologist, she will tell you that the rock is no less than a couple billion years old. Today scientists are proving their point, getting it right, and the powerful churches are pissed because they are pulling back the curtain on their fairy tales."

"You said 'yes on the earth and no on the universe;' meaning?"

"No, it did not take me six days to create the universe. I created the universe in less than one second. And within that one second the universe expanded to a million -"

"Miles?"

"- a million times a million times a million miles wide - and still growing."

"Wow!"

"Yeah...wow. Also, when it was expanding in the first few thousands of years it was a fireball of energy. It wasn't like it is now. Also if you know your chemistry, you know the building blocks of human life weren't even on Earth at the beginning, in fact the Earth wasn't here in the beginning. It took hundreds of thousands of years to create the earth and thousands more years to make it livable for human beings. It was all part of the developing soup."

"Okay so our universe was created by you 14.2 million -"

"-billion-"

"-billion years ago and it didn't take six days, it took about a second."

"Give or take a half a second."

"And the Earth was not created at the beginning of the universe, so that means man wasn't created either."

"Correct. But the Bible takes a few millions of years and collapses it into a one week for framing; easier for the reader to understand, probably? The whole thing with the: 'On the seventh day I rested' was also a whopper. It was written that way to make sure people showed up for church on Sunday instead boozing and ass grabbing. You can't collect money for the church if they don't show up."

"In Genesis, over that first week, and let's also remember they were not wearing digital watches so how did they know what a day was much less a week, I also was supposed to create a grown man and drop him into the Garden of Eden. Now I can appreciate that the people back then were winging this stuff so followers had a vision of where they had come from, but that doesn't change the fact that they could have adjusted the message as the theory of evolution was proved over the last couple hundred years. Not one peep about Darwin. No! They stand there like fools in the face of one of my greatest miracles and tell anyone and everyone that Adam and Eve just popped onto the planet."

"What 'greatest miracle'?"

"Life! To this day there is not a doctor or scientist who can tell you why your heart starts to beat. You want a miracle? I give you the beating heart."

"That is an awesome one."

"You want to know what makes that 10 ounce piece of muscle in your chest start to pump for no apparent reason?"

"Hell, yah!"

"Love, the energy of love: the mystery of life is the energy of love. The power of the universe. The energy you call love makes your ticker tick."

"Really?"

"Really! Now they can explain to you why it keeps beating, how it physically works and how they can restart it with a defibrillator but not how it boots up for the first time. Truth? Your heart is tapping into the power of the universe. Want another one of the big ones?"

"Sure."

"A living cell does this little trick of making itself two from one. For some reason, it grows beyond its structure and boom, a second cell. These two little miracles are the source and explanation of all human life. Pond scum, meet the electric power of the universe and whammo. We have you!"

God shoots me an evaluating look then stops.

176

"I don't think you are ready for the chemistry, I can tell. Let's get back to the garden of good and evil. Enter bad god."

He caught me with that deer-in-the-headlights look on my face. Shit!

"Slow down. Let me process so I can get it."

He pauses for a full second, but I can tell he is anxious to continue. You can tell he loves telling the story as if he knows it isn't true but he likes the bad-boy God sound of the stories. Odd that I am even thinking this. This is so fucking strange.

"Nah, let's get back to Adam and Eve. So, they are frolicking around the Garden of Eden, and for no apparent reason, I show up and tell them to do anything they want, but please don't eat any apples from this certain tree. Why? Why that tree? Why come down? Why come down and blow her shit? Of course the devil shows up and tempts her and since she was a simple, weak, mindless girl- and you know how the holy boys don't like girls - she was portrayed as the person who caused original sin because she couldn't deal with temptation. And now everyone, according to the Bible, everyone born, is born with original sin, and if you believe the rest of the story, if a baby dies before they are baptized they would go to hell. Where does that rank on your bullshit-o-meter?"

I shake my head.

"How can a pure, newborn baby have sin? And how can religion create original sin? Original sin? They start right at the beginning of your life making you feel like shit and you spend the rest of your life trying to EARN your way into heaven. It is a guilt-ridden mess. And it makes me sick."

"That does seem pretty harsh."

"Don't sweat it. It never happened, ever. The entire story was utter bull shit. Follow the lessons of the church or…"

He starts making a monster voice.

"…. I will become very mad and bring floods and fires and send babies to hell!"

He relaxes and lowers his voice.

"I hate the idea that they dump on the girls. As men we both know it is a crock, because woman can usually hold it together better than men. It's the men who succumb to temptation. And by the way, the apple and the devil in the Garden of Eden was one of many frequent metaphors in the Bible describing men trying to keep their sexual shit together either by blaming the devil, how convenient or ..."

"Women?"

"Women! I can't tell you how frustrating it is. All the crap about Eve coming from one of his ribs is male folly too. She came from one of his ribs? Bullshit! If anyone came from anywhere he came from his mama. People never just appear from an order of ribs. And what is truly comical, women, yes women, are the key to the growth of the universe. They are the center of the universe, and religions hardly mention them. And when they do they speak of women they are bit players or the rubes who screwed up the resort living for everyone in the Garden of Eden."

"Not all women were painted poorly. What about-"

"-The 'Virgin' Mary? The center of life in the universe is a WOMAN and her ability to create life, nurture life, feed life, and grow life from within in her womb, her body. And you know what moms do with new babies?"

"Love?"

"Yes! Love! And you now know what love evolves into?"

"Energy?"

"Yes! So who is the architect of the universe? Who is creating energy?"

"Women?"

"Yes! My boy! All over it. Finally!"

"And the buffoons; MEN! with their inferiority, short-dick complex that wrote the Bible, make Mary, the woman who bore me a virgin! The story of the Virgin Mary could not be farther from the truth. How can you read this with a straight face? Why can't sex be Godly? There is no shame in having sex. It's the jumper cables of life. Every

time I have arrived back here I was the son or daughter of my parents. And for these clerics to paint the beauty of motherhood and childbirth as the immaculate conception is disturbing and a slap in my face to the simple beauty and true miracle of life!"

I've got to move him off the subject or we'll be here all night. And I want to hear more.

"Okay, got it. Women are the center of the universe. What happens next?"

"Fuck, I almost forgot. I have Cain killing Abel to teach people about sin. A brother killing a brother? What a bunch of shit. That one really bugs me!"

He sits boiling. I can see him getting more and more pissed. Hate rushes across his brow like I have never witnessed since I met Him. Then He remembers I am standing there staring at Him and quickly recoils. You see Him mentally adjust his mindset and move on.

"Let's jump ahead 1,000 years. Noah's Ark...."

"I love this story! I remember in third grade religious-education class on Saturday morning, we had to clip magazine pictures of animals and bring them into class to put them in the ark, that we made from brown butcher paper. The ark had to be eight feet long to fit all our animals. And to a third grader it looked 50 feet long. It took us three weeks to build it."

"Well, at least you built one. Noah never did. As the story goes, God-Me-is tired of all the sinning in the world and tells Noah that I am going to kill everyone with a flood because they were all sinners; more pure and frightening bullshit! After I supposedly flooded the earth and killed everyone, I receded the waters and told Noah..."

He leans forward and goes into his best Elmer Fudd.

"I prowmiss wever, wever to do wis agween. I am sure Noah felt better hearing that coming from what, the heavens? By the way, who's left to grow the human race? Noah and his family? Again, like Adam and Eve, what kind of human race would come from the same parents and old farts to boot? It is all very weird shit. Now, on to the Tower of Babel. I notice people are not worshipping Me so God, Me..."

"You don't have to keep saying 'God, me' I get it."

179

Talk to God

"'I' give everyone different languages so they wouldn't be able to understand each other for sinning? Why? Why would I do that? Or just maybe the fool writing the story couldn't figure out that people from other parts of the world spoke different dialects? No, that would make too much sense. Let's just say I gave people different languages because they were not worshiping me. A crock! There! Bad God has spoken!"

"What's next?"

"I decide to have a personal relationship with Abraham. He's here on earth, I am up in heaven, but I talk to him directly, just booming out of the clouds or the other classic… I talk to him in his dreams. Whoa. How do I start the relationship? Mr. Nice God tells him to leave his wife and family. Next God and Abraham decide to wipe five cities off the face of the earth near the Jordan River because the cities are full of sinners: two being Sodom and Gomorra. Again God annihilates his children, I burn down the cities; obliterated them. What is that, the third time I administered genocide to my people in the first hundred pages? Are you noticing a pattern here?"

He's rolling now. This shit is truly dreary.

"For all Abraham's work, I give him a son, Isaac, when he is 130 years old. How did I celebrate his son's birth? I tell Abraham to prove his love for me by killing his son. Just as he is about to do it, I tell him to fuggedaboutit. Shit! What an asshole God. Want to keep going?"

God catches me waning.

"A little bit …. maybe. This shit is whacked."

"For the next few thousand years, The Old Testament follows Abraham's descendants through generation after generation, each with one twisted, guilt drenched, self-depriving chapter after another, until we end up in Egypt with the birth of Moses. If you can believe it, the story takes a turn for the worse. I decide not to speak to Moses from the clouds. I choose to speak to him through — ready for it? through a burning bush. Nothing says 'believe me, I am God' like combustible landscaping. Who makes up this stuff? I kind of liked it when I was speaking to people from the sky. It had a lot more style, some grandeur."

"I don't know who makes this up."

"Then God tells Moses to go to the Pharaoh of Egypt and tell him to set his people free!"

He does the 'set his people free' thing in a Martin Luther King voice - or at least tries to sound like that.

"But just all the Jewish people, that is. The Pharaoh tells him to stick it, and God sends down a plague to destroy the people of Egypt except for the Jewish people making the Jews the chosen few. Two million people follow Moses out of Egypt. Armies follow, and then I drown them all in the Red Sea."

"That's enough."

"Hold on. Allow bad God to finish. After all his work, dragging the Jews through the dessert for 40 years, Moses finally delivers everyone to the Promised Land. Then, here is my favorite part of the story as told by the church, I tell Moses that, 'Sorry, you can't come into the Promised Land' because you have sinned. What a bum deal. After all his work, I still don't forgive him. It gets more twisted. Just before Moses dies I show him the Promised Land, show him, not let him enter, but just show him. Then, according to the Old Testament he dies in my arms, and then I bury him. That's me: the old crypt keeper on Earth burying people."

"God, you were a prick."

"I didn't do anything of the sort. That's the problem with the Old Testament: It's all about deprivation, guilt, suffering, and saying you are sorry. What really blows my mind? It is totally the opposite of how it is supposed to be."

I think God needs a little teasing.

"So you chumped Moses?"

"What? I didn't chump anyone. It's all lies!"

"I am just kidding."

He doesn't care.

"According to 'The Book' I did! But none of that actually happened. The Jews did leave Egypt and went to the Gaza strip, but no Red Sea parting - actually there were heavy rains and some flooding, but the Egyptian soldiers were called back to Egypt after

181

Talk to God

Pharaoh decided it would be easier to feed his kingdom without two million hungry Jews. I am sure in the monsoon season, with the pouring rain and thousands of soldiers on their tail and all of them suddenly doing an about face, disappearing, it probably looked to someone that the seas swallowed them up but not true; they just turned around and went home. Add a few hundred years of time between when it happened and when it was rewritten and rewritten and rewritten and everything gets embellished. But that sure isn't as theatrical as Charlton Heston waving his arms and staff and having the sea part; much cooler and a better story to frighten the Jews into believing."

He continues to defend. I shouldn't have teased him.

"I think I have heard enough Old Testament."

"You sure? I haven't yet destroyed Jericho by sending a drought. I am good at droughts, Genocide, very dry with a twist."

"No that's cool; maybe next time."

"I've never counted, but I think I wiped out all the people on Earth six or seven times in the Old Testament. I have always wondered how you are all standing here talking if I wiped out the entire population so many times."

25

*"The Old Testament is a book of fiction written by frightened charlatans
just trying to keep the masses in line."*

"So why did they write it like this?"

*"The Old Testament is a book of fiction written by frightened charlatans just trying to
keep the masses in line."*

"Frightened? Of who? You?"

"No, frightened of the people they were controlling."

"Scaring them? That was their plan?"

*"Let's get something straight. I never spoke to any humans from the heavens. I can't even
do that if I tried, never ever. I never dictate my will. The only will here is, is free will.
What really occurred is the Jewish people walked out of Egypt and the leaders of the
Jewish people-Moses and his crew-replaced the Egyptian tyranny with me or stories of me,
bad God. It is total bullshit, but fear of God, or as they put it in the Old Testament,
'not in my favor,' is what kept the leadership in charge."*

*"To me, I thought religion was going to be the public relations department of my message
instead of how these bozos built it to frighten people. Shit. Too bad you all got going in
the wrong direction with that stupid book. Love is the answer, not hate and fear. They
knew it, and they kept lying to continue to hold onto the power. If they would have led*

people with love, everyone would have really dug the message and would have followed for all the right reasons. Look at you and me."

There is a huge, pregnant, dead-silence pause. God stares at me thinking I am just going to respond positively... or did he? Am I again being emotionally evaluated? I freeze. I don't know why I froze. I start to think, do I love this man? Is this God, the God we were all taught to love because we were told he loves us? Who is this man? Do I really love him? Sure I guess I do, he gave me back a reason to live. Did he? Or am I hallucinating? Shit! Do I love my homeless God? I didn't know if I could love anyone or anything anymore. I do feel a shallow urge to love him, not pity though. Weird. It's been an emotional last 36 hours, but I never felt I gravitated that close to him, not yet. Do I love? Have I? Curiosity, yes; thankfulness, yes; appreciation, yes; but love? He grows uneasy. He leans forward, his face sullen.

"You love me, don't you? Or have you forgotten how to give your heart to others?"

God goes on the offense. Fuck! It is one of his tests. I knew it.

"Have you lost the ability to forgive, to nurture, to smile? Are you so scarred, in such pain, such dread, that you forgot what it is to share love? Haven't I showed you enough? Love is all around you. Love back. Can't you give love me back? Well, can you? Can you share love? Have you lost all love? You have to learn to give again? You have to learn to love again? Have you lost the feeling of love, to share love, to give love? Well, have you? HAVE YOU?"

He stands up. I didn't think it could happen but the expression on His face crumbles further into a darker, broken, sadness.

"No, you haven't. It's in there."

He taps his chest. I swell with heart ache. My pain now wells from within. It is like He is drawing it out of me, as if He was sucking snake venom from my arm from a bite mark.

"I am empty! It was taken from me. Was that part of the big plan: ruining my life and killing my wife?"

His eyes fill with tears. There is silence.

"Haven't you been listening? I don't plan! I don't plan dick!"

"Yes but, FUCK! It hurts so bad!"

He locks eyes with me. I turn away. A huge charge of energy rushes from my chest to the top of my head. It makes me lightheaded, dizzy. I feel the desire to go to him. He is drawing me to him now. I can feel it, something I know I cannot control, magnetized. My pain tells me to fight against it, maybe just to see if I could. Fuck! What am I doing? What is happening to me? I just don't know how much hate is harbored in my soul. Consciously or unconsciously, I am being drawn to turn myself back around to face him and look into his eyes. I rotate slowly. I am not in control. His stare is intoxicating; hypnotic.

"You and I? There is love in your heart. There is love for me and for everyone-still. Look deep; find it. Push away the hate. It is so important for you to do this NOW!"

I can't pull away. God drops his chin to his chest and slumps into a baseball catcher's position, still leaning on the side of the book case. He closes his eyes and puts his head in his hands.

Eyes closed or not, with some Star Wars tracking beam, I am being sucked to him, not physically, but mentally, emotionally. Every impulse, every urge, every strand of instinct, my entire consciousness is being consumed, and he draws me to him. I do everything to fight the feeling. Do I test him? Or should I go to him? I want to test him.

"Are you God! Are you? Are you the loving God?"

"Why are you asking this?"

Maybe I want Him to test me. Show me You are God! Let's see what you got! I mentally snap free, or He lets me. I break the hypnotic bond for a moment. I seize the chance to seek proof he being God.

"…I have to tell you 'God:' I don't feel the love. I hear what you are saying, but I feel pain and emptiness right now."

"You are in great, evil pain. Work past it. Please! I love you!"

"Where is the love train for me? Why do I feel so alone? How can I find and share in the love that you speak of? How do I stop the pain that is now me? My fucking pain is palpable! I breathe, I spit, I bleed, I sweat fucking pain! Why in the fuck am I following you around? I am fucking broken! I am a FUCKING BROKEN MAN!"

I watch his tears slip down his cheeks, sticking to three-day-old beard littered with food and dirt. They mix with the residue, changing the tears to a dirt dark solution, woman-like when make-up runs, continuing down to his chin and then down his neck, finally settling on his collar. He blinks and wipes his eyes. He looks up, up into my sullen eyes, my broken heart. He smiles a sad clown, disappointed smile. He reaches out his right hand toward me. I feel this odd-ice-pick, chill race up my spine to the back of my neck, stronger and throughout my entire head, then through my shoulders and down to my finger-tips. He's not playing now. The gravitating sensation seems to be falling out of me through the tips of my fingers toward him. The hair on my arms stands up. He motions for me to take His hand. I try to resist.

"No!"

I begin to scream!

"I want to know without your tricks! Do You love me? Does anyone love me anymore? Can I love again? Does the world love me too God? Is there love left in the universe for me?"

186

My eyes well up with tears and begin to stream down my face. I quiver in uncontrollable spasm. He whispers under his breath.

"I love you. Many, many people love you!"

"But it hurts so much right now! Where is my love? It shouldn't hurt this much to love! I am fucking broken and bleeding!"

He reaches for me again. I start to sob, trying not to outwardly cry.

"No! Don't! Don't touch me! I don't want her to see me like this anymore!"

He springs up out of his catcher's position, grabs my hand, and pulls me toward him with violent force, and hugs me tightly. I couldn't move or free myself if I chose to.

"This is NOT from her. This…this is Me, this is you, 'THIS' is the universe. This is My love."

I don't know how it feels to be electrocuted, but this must come close. He strengthens His grip around my chest and arms. In a breath I am now paralyzed with what should be described as electricity, maybe, but I do not die. The sensation begins to increase, turbines churning, adding the wetness of an ocean wave not hitting me, but rushing through me. Water? No. Energy maybe; rushing through with sheer velocity. I try to glance down to see if I am wetting myself again. No. The sensation starts at the top of my chest where we were meshed together the closest, then flows, continually over and through every pore, every nerve, and every sense in my body, down to my feet and back to the top of my head in a continual cycle. I have lost the feeling of my physical beginning and ending. I am a conduit, opened at the top and the bottom, energy flushing through me at an enormous rate. From the top of my head to the back of my heels, the electric rush and wetness of an ocean of supercharged energy cascades, through me. Shit!

The sensation increases in pace and velocity. I begin to feel translucent, vaporous, free of my body and at the same time an equal part of Him. He is here. I am there. We are one. I look at my hands and arms to see if they are still there. They are. I am losing the physicality of my being. Now wind, vastness, I feel opened, turned inside out, wide, consuming, fast. Wind vaporizes the feeling of water. The sensation, the perception and weight of water is too dense a conductor for my pace. Fuck! Yes, it is wind. Is it wind? It's too fast. I am moving beyond the ability for my eyes to see what I am passing. I'm riding the mushroom cloud of nuclear energy. No, I am not riding it, I *am* it. It's moving too fast now for a nuclear explosion. I am thinner and faster than wind. I can no longer control my body. What body? My emotions flicker. I am now spirit without flesh. I have passed beyond myself, but I am feeling. I am feeling safe, at ease, and it feels wonderful, truly wonderful.

God reaches around with His left hand and cups the back of my head. I feel his hand, so I must be still within my physical being if I am watching it happen away from myself. He draws my head to his shoulder so his mouth is right at my ear.

"I love you so much. Feel my love. Feel the love in the universe that surrounds you. And please do not forget to breathe."

"What?"

He clenches me tighter. The energy running through me throttles up again. I didn't think it possibly could. I struggle to describe it now; the feeling doubles, then triples. There is no stress, no tight weary muscles, no worries, no pain, and no cold memories. I feel no aches, no creeks, and no soreness. I physically do not feel any longer, but I am mentally here. I am now the purest of energies. Oh shit! I am moving with it. It is me. I am it!

"Breathe…please breathe."

Am I breathing? The senses that would tell me I am breathing are no longer at my disposal. I try to remember what I

188

did to breathe, how to open my mouth; I tell my mind to navigate the process. I think. I think I am breathing. I try to speak.

"Is… this…how… it…is… to…die?"

My mouth does not move, remaining closed.

"No, this is how it is to live, to love, to live after you evolve and to love. LOVE!"

It dawns on me that we are speaking to each other, but we are not speaking aloud. We are talking, no, communicating now without speaking. But am I… speaking through thought?

"Hold on to me now."

Another tightening squeeze and the feeling throttles up again to another level. I couldn't even imagine it becoming stronger much less tripling like this. The feeling of electricity, rushing water, wind, whatever it is-has accelerated beyond the point of any physical feeling. Now it's lighter, airier, the feeling has much less friction: quicker, faster than, than what? Sound? Light? The speed of light? Am I moving at light speed? But I am still. Am I?

Again it increases. It moves through me now so fast at quantum velocity. The sensation of energy flowing through me is replaced with the sensation that I am now the energy. It, me, we, begin to lose any sound I perceived I was hearing. I feel lighter, even lighter, flashing energy, faster and quicker but I am not moving. Am I? I am thinking, moving, where I think, I am moving now where I think, processing, everything quicker than anything I could ever perceive or process on Earth. Decades of growth, memories, memories of mine flash past me, or through me, in fractions of a second.

Oddly, I can control the information flow. I am … I am … I think I have, no, I know, I have become pure emotional, intellectual, loving? Energy. It is amazing! Is it? Is it light energy? God, it is the purest of feeling, euphoria is too pale of a word to describe it. I never want to let it go. I am energy now moving at

189

the speed of light. I am being flung across what? The universe. No, I am not being flung across the universe; I am, yes, I am, yes, fuck! I am a connected part of it! Oh shit! I am moving with it. It is me. I am it! Oh God, it is pure nirvana: a continual explosion of energy cycling through me, but there is no me. I think therefore I am. But what am I? I know I am presently not human.

My God! What have I become? Have I died? Have I crossed over? Have I evolved? My God have I begun, have I become a part … a part of the universe that you speak of? Yes? That's it! Yes! I am! I see the vision of God staring at me, a warm smile glowing from the corners of His eyes. He nods his approval. I begin to get comfortable with my being. It feels, no, it is, pure bliss, convulsing, orgasmic, bliss.

"Last evolution. Remember to breathe."

Another one? Fuck! I can't tell if I am breathing. Last evolution? Oh shit! I accelerate again; faster and faster again. The speed and quickness I feel is no longer measured or described in the physicality of flow, water, wind, electricity or friction but in slight changes in my thought. There is a quickness about my feelings now, an ability to move, to be anywhere, everywhere instantly wherever I imagine it. I can move freely with no restraints of humanness or the friction of speed. That has all been dissolved. I can go anywhere, any plane, any soul, all energy levels with, which I assume travel at the same velocity as the universe I now have become part of. Have I? I can be anything. I can be everything. I am in God. I am God now. I am with her. I am in her. I am a child again. Fun! I am exploring! I am conscious energy! I am everywhere! I am everything! I am anything!

"I am!"

"Yes, you are, and this is 'true love.' This is unbridled love. This is the love that drives you, that makes your heart beat, draws you to love and share love and expands the universe. This is energy. This is the love you will share with Me and…her, and everyone who share your love. This is the process of your evolution. "

Oh, true bliss!

"I'm going to start letting you go now."

"No! No! This is it! I need this! Please! Take me now God! I love you! I really do! Take me now! I am ready to leave. There is nothing here! I am ready to evolve. Take me, God! Take me now!"

"This isn't for you now. Soon, soon enough. Remember: share this love."

I try to hold on to him tight now. I fight for his grip.

"When I let you go, this is going to feel different."

He starts to relax his grip around my arms and back. All the speed, the turbines of energy begin to slow and disappear. The weight of my humanness begins to crush my head, neck, and chest. I begin to feel my limbs and being. I weigh ten times my body weight. I am soaked with human heaviness.

"Hold on now. It is going to get tougher."

I try to find my feet, my balance. I can't. I slump in His arms. I am scraping down His chest and midsection until I find myself on my knees in front of him holding on to his waist wishing for the ride to never end.

"I think I got this."

"Really? You got it?"

I can't balance my body on my knees.

"…No I don't."

I can't feel my legs yet, and I crumple to the floor. I cough. I am taking my first breath and the air passing through my mouth feels thick and heavy, chewable, odd. The feeling of weight, possibly gravity, is enormous.

"Breathe."

I feel asthmatic. I am gagging, struggling for air. I am having trouble reacquainting myself with my being. I fall into a heap and just close my eyes. I am exhausted. I am disappointed and very human again. Dark, silence, sleep.

26

That is what humans will evolve to. That is your afterlife.
That is your heaven - and I haven't had one complaint.

I awake curled up in a fetal heap, the same position I must have passed out in. All my limbs feel like I slept on them. Any movement makes my extremities tingle. As I blink open my eyes I find myself and try to find my bearings. I am in a puddle of sweat. Soaking wet up and down the front of me where we were touching when he was holding me. I get to my hands and knees. God is now sitting at a library study table next to where I was on the floor. He is smiling at me.

"Ha-a-a-a-a-ow... l-l-l-l-longa – ga – ga ha-ha-ha-ha ve I-I-I b-b-b-been out-t-t-t-?"

"Thirty minutes. How do you feel? I thought I might have lost you there for a bit."

"Re-....lee? I-I-I-I fee.... li....ke-ke-ke-ke .... Sh-sh-sh-shi-it."

"It will pass."

My mouth has trouble forming words. I think I sound drunk, but my ears are ringing so I am not sure. I decide not to talk and think what I want to say like I caught us doing before.

I THINK: "So that is evolving? That's where everyone goes? That is where I am eventually going, where my wife is, where everybody goes?"

God answers me out loud.

"I took you about halfway."

Son of a bitch-it works! This is fucking cool.

I THINK: "Serious?"

"It is cool, and I am serious. If you would have totally evolved it would have destroyed your body's ability to sustain your life, your soul."

I THINK: "But that is where people go; where my wife went?"

"Yes if they loved. The strength of the energy you felt is based and fueled on the love you share, remember?"

I THINK: "Was all that energy my love?"

"You were helping but it was not equal. Your love, my friend, is strong, but you have to find it again-and you have a long way to go."

I THINK: "Can I go back?"

"Not until it is time."

I THINK: "When is my time?"

"I don't know. There is no predetermined moment for you. I have no idea when you will come. Free will is free will. My only recommendation would be to live life and love, which you have not been doing. In fact you have been hating. Not cool. When you love, it will make your evolution and existence at the next level more amazing. I don't want to give you too much to swallow, but the greater amount of love you share, let's say you share love with hundreds of thousands of people, that love, that energy will give you the ability to...."

God stops speaking and begins to internally process his next statement. My speech returns as quickly as it left me. I slink into the chair across from him at the library table, and I feel funky, the front of me is soaking wet - and now cold.

"To what? Ability to do what?"

"It's too much for you to handle."

"Please! What! You have to tell me!"

"If you love enough ..."

I watch him ponder and become vexed.

"Nope, forget it."

"Please?"

"No, not now. You'll figure it out soon enough."

"Well, then answer me one question."

"Sure, if I can or want to answer it. But if one human, in this case- you- has the knowledge of your evolution and no one else does, and you share this information, you will be chastised, treated like a loon. Trust me; I know what I am talking about. Some things when you evolve are not supposed to be known by humans presently, are best left alone for a bit, but fire."

"Did I evolve into pure energy?"

"What?"

I surprised him.

"Did I actually become energy, love, you know? Part of the expanding universe?"

"Well..."

195

Talk to God

God begins to stammer.

"Well-well-you see- well."

"Ohh shit! Ohh holy shit!"

An epiphany.

"Alright hold on. You did not totally evolve. Remember the body thing? But, like I said, I took you halfway there."

"But was I or did I just become living proof of Einstein's theory?"

"What? What theory? And who is Einstein?"

"Don't shit me. I'm an educated man, and so are you. Einstein! You know: E=MC2; That Einstein!"

Dead silence. I see him thinking, surely processing his answer and my ability to understand it.

"I know Einstein very well."

"Then was I, well was I? Was I mass at the speed of light cubed thus evolving back into pure energy like he said we could?"

There was no less than 30 seconds of silence. It felt like five minutes. I could tell he was deciding if he was willing to answer my question. Shit! I think I got this. A wide grin comes over God's face, a twinkle sparkled in the corner of his eye.

"I got it! No! Fucking! Way!"

God smiles rocks up in his chair, now sitting straight up on its edge, professor like, enjoying watching his star pupil solving a complex equation.

"Well, look who's getting it! You are the first human who is close to connecting the dots. The difference is and this is going to be hard for you; Einstein's theories were infantile, because he didn't consider the conscious or intellectual elements of the expansion of the

196

universe. He never walked it out to the end. From a spiritual perspective Einstein was as simple-minded as the clerics and high priests were in relation to science; they were polar opposites and so firm in their beliefs, they never thought there could be a third option; a hybrid if you will. Einstein was beginning to get the science side of it correctly. Religious leaders were stuck in the dark with their stories."

"Were any of the 'stories' close? Did any of the high priests, clerics, or open minded spiritualists ever perceive or even ask you about the science being tied in with the spiritual, with the love and energy?"

"Are you serious? I can't tell you how many times I tried telling them. I told you that earlier. When I came as Jesus of Nazareth, I explained it all to them in very simple terms. They just never could deal with the science. Deal is not the right word. They couldn't understand it... at all."

"Religious leaders missed the real spirituality of it. It's out there. I told them many times that the science and the spirituality were one. But what little they were getting from, either messages from me throughout the generations or just good guessing; they could never believe that the biology and chemistry of the universe could also, truly be what they were spiritually seeking. They just have too much invested in the make-believe stories, and too much to lose if those stories were incorrect, so they stayed with that book over there."

"The budding scientific minds- Einstein, Darwin, Hubble, even Sagan- dismissed the conscious, emotional, intellectual, and spiritual side of the science: the soul and spirit's ability to evolve to the next level through a scientific process while the priests never imagined it possible to have a scientific explanation of the spirituality they were seeking."

God stands up and raises his voice.

"AND THERE, RIGHT SMACK DAB IN THE MIDDLE OF THEM BOTH IS THE TRUTH: BOTH HALF RIGHT AND BOTH HALF WRONG!"

God slams his hand, karate chop style, hard on the large table.

"God, I feel stupid."

"Don't. It's pretty heady stuff and you seem to be getting it."

197

"Was Einstein that smart?"

"He was truly advanced, but not a super brain. I figured he was 10,000 years more advanced than his peers in scientific matters. He was young and looking for girls when we met. He was a bright and interesting guy. His papers on relativity were pointing the wagons of reality in the right direction. After he got published, his career took off, took positions at universities including Brussels and Princeton. Then he became anything he wanted. The odd request was Israel asking him to be President. But he was the right guy for me at the time - or at least I thought he was."

"What do you mean 'right guy'?"

"Did you dig the last hour when I held you and showed you the true power of love, the fuel of the universe?"

"You mean when we did the thing? …. Heck yes, I dug it! Let's go again!"

He pauses and offers up another smirky smile.

"…so did he."

"Are you shitting me?"

"I told you you were going to be amazed."

"It's unbelievable! So he got the ride? I thought he was just working from a philosophical perspective, the science! "

"I walked him through everything. He didn't swear as much as you, though most of our conversations were in German."

God comfortably slides into German dialect.

"Sind Sie, mich vollscheißend."

"What does that mean?"

"One of your favorite quotes: Are you shitting me?"

"Funny. So Einstein wrote E=mc2 because you proved it to him?"

198

"Sort of. There were a few guys getting close when I met him in 1903, but he was just theorizing; we worked on it for a while. I was so excited that someone was getting near the reality I really gravitated to him and was dying to show him. He was the right guy, friendly, interesting, funny and outgoing. When his first paper was published he was like a rock star. He changed everything Newton, Galileo, and von Leibniz had written back in the 1700s. You must know though, there were two published works by him on this subject, one in 1905 and the other in 1915."

"Why?"

"He struggled with what I told him, and he kept trying to get it right or rationalize it again away from the spiritual side. He never grasped conscious, loving energy to his dying days in the 1950s. I give him credit, he was putting the scientific pieces together, and I was filling in the spiritual, love, energy side. He originally didn't believe me until I showed him. As I said he stopped at the science, and I had to press him into the reality of love, the real energy. He just didn't want to believe it."

"So its not E=MC2 but ..."

"Love!"

"L equals M C squared not E?"

"Yeah, too bad he was just too much of a scientist, a scarred realist. I wish he had been more opened minded. I could have actually used him to be a bit more of a dreamer; a little more spiritual, but I thought he was the right guy to get word out."

"Why?"

"He was the farthest thing removed from a priest or religious leader. In fact, the impact of his theories brought outcry from many religious organizations, especially the Catholic and Jewish faiths. Because of his frustration at trying to put his arms around the spiritual and conscious energy of the universe he was an atheist. But here is the thing: He was an atheist based on the stories and teachings in the Bible. He was actually NOT an atheist and struggled with being an agnostic. The ride I gave him probably just confused what he had already determined was the truth."

"And that was?"

"That there was no God but a big bang. There was a guy named Baruch Spinoza in the 1700s who believed the God in the Bible did not exist, and was one of the first, what was termed a 'rationalist,' which eventually led to the thinking of the 1900s called 'the Age of Enlightenment.'"

"These were the scientific thinkers sticking their noises into the argument that the God in the Bible is not reality. I can't tell you how much I loved it. I finally thought they were getting it. Most of those free thinkers like Spinoza, who was a Dutch Jew, were excommunicated. None of the religious folks liked what he and others were saying. Because his theories were so radical, his work was dismissed until well after his death. So when Einstein was getting it I thought finally, we will be getting the truth out there, not from a priest or a rabbi but a scientist. He just couldn't process the idea that there the truth in the middle melding the spiritual with the science."

"Wow! Son of a bitch! Amazing. So our evolution is that we become the universe. Love is the energy that drives and fuels the universe?"

"Finally! In simple terms, yes."

"And you showed or helped Einstein by showing him what you showed me?"

"Everyone needs a little nudge. I also thought being a realist, a scientist, a pragmatist would be the perfect voice and that people would believe him because he wasn't a cleric or priest or religious freak, but a typical academic from the other side of the argument. He just never finished the sentence for me tying the love to the science. He believed me. But he knew they would think he was nuts if he ties in the human element…"

"-the love!"

"…yes, the love. Because they knew the scientific truth of the universe, they dismissed all God, heaven, the afterlife stories. Einstein, Aristotle, Galileo, Newton, Spinoza and even Darwin with evolution, all the great minds in the past, just never thought there may be a third explanation, one that does not include 'just' a God, or one that includes 'just' science. Einstein and the church for, as far apart as they were, they had one thing on common: They couldn't connect the dots from each of their perceptions to the others."

"Fuck me. Okay, cool, got it as much as I can get it today without being Einstein. Just one more time on the connection thing with others."

"The more people who you share this energy with…"

"…love."

"…yes. The more people you share love with, the stronger your level of energy can become when you evolve. It compounds and supports each other's energy."

God points directly at me.

"How strong?"

"Real strong. Again you think that you need to go out and have some emotional relationship with millions of people. You just need to connect and share the warmth of caring. There is strength and power in numbers."

"Wait then. Let me ask you one other question…please!"

God shoots me a wicked smile.

"Go ahead."

"Was that heaven?"

"That is what humans will evolve to. That is your afterlife. That is your heaven - and I haven't had one complaint."

"It is glorious and beyond anything I could have imagined."

"You are part of the expanding universe. You are all part of me, and I am part of you, and all are part of each other. It is what you all on earth refer to as heaven. Yes, it is the place people evolve to. It is heavenly."

"And if you don't love: No energy?"

"Yes."

"But if you hate…"

"…like you, right now."

Talk to God

The statement freezes me. Fuck! I have been hating.

"... I was thinking more like Adolf Hitler"

"Okay?"

"If someone hates and shares hate, that reduces energy, reduces love?"

"Yes. You have the other side figured out too. Hitler? Dick. Those are the days I wish I was a vengeful god. I would have annihilated him with the power of the universe. The guy's a cock sucker, and he got what he deserved, and he is now alone. Everyone hated him, and hate creates loneliness after they evolve."

I see God shudder and tear up. He sits quietly, with his head in his hands, for a few minutes. He is silently crying. I assume he is mourning the victims of Hitler and the Holocaust. Seems I scratched a scab that still hurts. I can tell I truly upset him conjuring up these memories. The weight he must carry, that of the world, the universe. All those people, those victims, praying to Him, and He knowing it, and he can do nothing. What an odd and new concept.

We need to help each other. I know this now. The power of salvation is in our hands. Wow! What a fucking thought. Heavy. I understand now why he believes we are not ready to carry that information. He composes himself again, lifts his head, teary eyed and smiles.

"Sorry."

"Its cool. Are you okay?"

He nods yes.

27

Gabriel says to Mohammad,
"All the teachings of Moses and Jesus are incorrect."
I guess that part is close to the truth but I digress.

"So there is a hell where these guys go?"

"If hell to you would mean being alone in the universe, devoid of love and with limited energy, I guess there is a hell. But there is no hell with fire and guys with horns, tails, and pitchforks."

God smiles thinking of human's version of hell.

"The stories of heaven and hell have been created by people here guessing, the scarier the better keeping folks in order I showed you heaven, and I have been showing people the same thing, trying to explain to them what happens when you evolve and the importance of loving each other for almost every generation since you stood up on two feet. It just keeps coming out sideways in tribal stories, science fiction tales, religious adaptations..."

He nods and points toward the Bible.

"....I just wish someone would get it right and write it down correctly one of these days since I seem to have to repeat myself over and over and over again, ad nauseum. I am a bad storyteller I guess."

"I could do it."

Talk to God

"Really?

God blurts out a laugh.

"We'll see how you feel about that after I'm gone. Most people who have tried in the last number of generations are thought to be nuts, hanging by a thread onto the lunatic fringe; or if they attempt to share these teachings and disseminate them too widely, they are killed. It's tough being a disciple today."

"Well I'm sold. I'll gladly share my experiences."

"Great! Within months you will probably be jobless, homeless, and living with me on the street. You got to remember, these people…"

He points all around in a circle over his head referencing the present human race.

"…. are a couple generations removed from being simple apes. Decisions are made by the people with the biggest swords. Common sense doesn't yet exist. Even today the churches want the 'god' they worship to be a real ass kicker. They want a god who wields the power of the universe, controls the sun and the skies, and threatens humans - a twisted adaptation of the myths of Greek gods, making me a fire and brimstone god. By the way, brimstone is burning sulfur. You didn't ask before. A dick God patches a lot of holes in things they don't understand."

"For instance?"

"Anytime a tornado, hurricane, eclipse, sandstorm, meteor, asteroid, earthquake, or volcanic eruption would come crashing into their world, the church or leaders of people would tell the masses 'it was the wrath of God'. Name the bad weather event or celestial screw up, and it was me being pissed off. Every time lightning struck or thunder cracked it was God being mad. What a load of weather crap."

"If a child dies, or a famous person or political leader suddenly perishes, it was an act of God, or God has a plan, or God needed them in heaven. Wrong! No way, no how! Free will is free will. But since it's easier to move on and heal pain with some stupid 'Wrath of God' fixation, what does it matter? That's why they needed their god to be an unforgiving god or a god who threatens consequences in the stories in the bible. Weather doesn't stop because you pray for it to do so. Children are not brought back from the dead

204

because you prayed for them. But worship me and be a good citizen to the sitting king, and God will shine his favor on you. I wish I had the time."

God's starting to ramble and pout.

"But know that I have never done anything like that and don't possess the power or ability to change the weather or to force My divine power on humans, unless I am standing there speaking to them like we are now. So I guess I am a loving God. I guess you could say My love is extended to everyone by not getting involved or screwing with people's lives. I am the perfect parent to a world of teenagers. I can't control what you do."

"When you were on Earth as Jesus, you must have really gotten your message across. They wrote the New Testament based on that trip to Earth."

You can tell he likes the Jesus reference. Funny, God gets happy about one of his more popular times on Earth. His facial expression perks up; a glowing child about to get his name called to answer a question he knows well. God can be so human sometimes.

"It was a good run. I even had a name for the teachings and everything. I called My few messages, The Way. It caught on for awhile before they didn't like the beauty and simplicity of it."

What happened?

"What happened? Well, that's one part they all got right in all the books. They killed me. I don't think they really believed me anyway. They liked the big Hollywood stories: the thunder, the lightning, the floods. I was talking about finding love and God by looking inward. That didn't go over too well. Plus they couldn't even imagine or process what I was speaking about: the power of the universe, love; they thought they were in the center of the universe. They also thought the Earth was flat and every time thunder crashed I was displeased at them. Try talking intelligently to someone that believes that God is a finger snap away from flooding the earth for the umpteenth time. Back to my point: It has only been in the last few decades that I can share the truth about the universe without people looking at me like I am from another world - another world! Haaaa!"

205

God busts out in a big laugh, since I guess he WAS from this world. I need to get him back on message.

"So 'The Way' never really caught on?"

"They killed me before it got too big. Then they wrote that book of fairy tales…"

He again flicks his hand toward the huge Bible across the walkway.

"… the way they wanted it. Well, not right away. I will say though that The New Testament was a lot closer to the message of love, but as you feather through it, you can tell whoever wrote it just didn't get what I was saying. And the true comedy of it all is that it keeps changing through the generations to adapt to the present audience."

"I thought the Apostles wrote it? Were there Apostles?"

"There is no way I had a crew roll with me the way it is described in there, when I was doing what I'm doing now, when I was Jesus. There would be a few guys with me for a bit and then another few guys would join in but very few who stayed with me all the time. First they all thought they were going to be killed so they all ran for it. Then after the dust settled, some continued to preach when they saw it was cool to be part of the legend, to be one of Jesus' chosen ones who walked the earth with Jesus. Give me a break."

Again the quote fingers when he says Jesus.

"Next thing you know everybody started coming out of the wood work claiming to be one if my chosen disciples. Guys I never met. Guys that were with me maybe for a day started claiming to be one of my chosen disciples. I didn't choose anyone. I chose no one. Now there are eighteen guys claiming to have been one of my Apostles. It was bull shit. I think there were probably 4 that were steady but Phillip, Simon the Zealot? Who were these guys?"

"What about Judas"

"The same thing, he had as much to do with me as Mark David Chapman did. Why is it when you kill someone well known they use the murderers three names? Judas was a punk that was hanging around for a bit. Did you know there were gospels according to Judas."

"Really."

"Written by someone else and then the high priests junked it one hundred and eighty years later. So he didn't make the book of lies. They liked Judas just being a dick. He was."

"Wow. No commandments and no 12 Apostles?"

"Really funny?

"What?"

"I never, ever saw anyone write down what I was saying. Never. And it is the same exact stuff I am telling you. But no 12 Apostles. Heck, I guess you are one of Apostles this time around. But how they landed on twelve I don't know. They just wanted to get fame when my message stuck."

"What do you mean stuck?"

"The things I am telling you yesterday and today are exactly, exactly what I told them. NO DIFFERENT. Then I get killed and off they went writing that crap. Do you find what I have told you that complicated that it takes a book that big to explain?"

"No? Well I guess not."

"The simple message of love was expanded to all that over there."

God again waves at The Bible.

"You see my simple story of love had no one in charge. No fear. No guilt. No heaven or hell, just love each other. And if you did love each other you would enjoy being part of the loving energy of the universe. The big problem with that is that it would have ended religion as you know it and the high priests couldn't have that. So, ironically, the church told God to take a hike and they still do to this day so they can run the charade of religion. They just don't believe me when I keep returning. But I don't fault them too much. It's hard to believe one guy showing up talking about things that fly in the face of hundreds of years of beliefs. My day will come though."

"What about the other religions? Did they get it closer to the truth with their books?"

Talk to God

"Like the Qur'an?"

"Yeah."

"Hey, before I answer, I've got to tell you a story about the Bible and the Qur'an in the main branch of the public library in London. There is a big stink because the King James Bible is located on a higher shelf than the Qur'an. The only reason was that the books were shelved in descending alphabetical order: B coming before Q, no other reason. The Muslims get pissed so they move the Qur'an to the shelf above the Bible. The Christians move the Qur'an back to the lower shelf. The next day the Bible completely disappears and the Qur'an is the only book that remains. To make a dumb story dumber, there are actual fights breaking out, protests and gunfire because of the location of the books on the shelf! Both wrong. Does that sound stupid to anyone else? The two holy books and their followers can't agree on what stupid book shelf they belong on. Neither is written well- both are full of lies - and they fight over their placement in a library."

"What's your spin on the Qur'an?"

"It, too, is great fiction - better than the Bible."

"Really?"

"Yeah, my boy Mohammad, back around 610 A.D. in Mecca is said to have heard a voice as he was meditating. The voice said, 'You are the messenger of God.' Mohammad decided that this was the angel Gabriel. His friends tell him that he is the Arabic version of Moses for the Jews and Jesus for the Christians. Why not? That's how all the other religions got started. From the first message until his death, Mohammad's writings were collected and put in chapters and those chapters became the Qur'an. There are 30 chapters and 114 Surahs. Before you ask: Surahs are like the paragraphs in the chapter. But check out the story. You're going to love this one."

God switches ass cheeks on the chair and leans in to ensure my attention. But oddly he now whispers and scans the library to make sure that no one can hear him speak.

"Gabriel says to Mohammad: All the teachings of Moses and Jesus are incorrect: I guess that part is close to the truth, but I digress. So where was I? Oh, Gabriel speaks to Mohammad saying that God has sent me to you to get the story straight. So grab a

pencil, and we will get everything on paper. Over the next 20 years Mohammad cranks out the Qur'an based on messages from Gabriel."

"If you read the Qur'an, like the Bible, it is heavy-handed toward men. Women are treated poorly and described like dirt or property in society. In the Qur'an they are barely better than the house pet. Some female highlights from the Qur'an - and these are just a few: menstruation is a sickness, a woman is one half of a man, lewd woman are confined to their homes until death or are stoned to death, woman are feeble and are unable to devise a plan, or think, or process with any common sense. There is also the mutilation of a woman's sex organ to prevent her natural lasciviousness from taking over."

"This is typical guy, short penis, doesn't feel appreciated, bullshit. Women are the center of life, and these idiots are removing body parts and sewing up others. Why? Because in every man's heart they know the truth about woman being the source of life, and it kills them, so they create crap like in the Qur'an and The Bible."

"Why do woman stand for it if they hold all the cards?"

"Because part of the nature of a woman is to nurture, accept, support, and love regardless of their environment. It is what makes them powerful: the ability to navigate through all adversity and still continue to grow life and eventually the universe. Over time books like the Bible and Qur'an will be dismissed as you evolve emotionally and intellectually. The fact that people today, who I think are pretty bright, still believe it, swear by it, and in some cases die supporting it, is just foolishness and counterproductive to moving humans closer to the truth about love. If you all in today's society saw the jokers who were writing this stuff years ago, you would dismiss them all as fourth grade level, short stories written by the lunatic fringe. Utter nonsense."

"I can't believe anyone would even dream any of that stuff up for a person, especially a woman. Did Mohammad not like women? Was he a closet homosexual in his time?"

"On the contrary, he had game. He had nine wives and a girlfriend on the side. The dude was a player. If you take the time to rationalize all religions and the guys who wrote the books, it's all about sex, actually men's self-confidence issues about sex. It's all dick issues. The Qur'an is full of pure twisted excuses for sexual abuse: the rule book for the ultimate boys' night out. How they talk about women is shameful. The Bible is just as bad in the opposite way: They hardly mention women. And when they do, you have no real, main, female characters unless they are virgins in trouble, prostitutes, or just some vessel to explain how one of these oafs mentioned in the Bible or the Qur'an got here."

209

"Did Mohammad have children?"

"This is the real kicker. After writing the Qur'an that describes women as a little higher on the food chain than the family cat, he and his nine wives have four children- ALL GIRLS!"

God roars with laughter!

"All girls: The boys they had never made it out of childbirth or were stillborn. I had nothing to do with any of it, if you were thinking of asking. Mohammad wrote chapters in the Qur'an to deal with his personal wifely and sexual appetite. Imagine, he wrote that God gave him his own set of rules and the rest of the Muslim world a different set in regards to dealing with women and screwing around; how bloody convenient."

"What were the big differences?"

"Well, the difference in the rules boils down to HE can have many woman, take them as his wives, have girlfriends and still be married while the other Muslim men could not. God told Mohammad and only Mohammad that 'he' could screw around. Everyone else had to stay in line!"

"They all believed that?"

"Read it someday. By the way, Mohammad thought male sperm came from your kidney not your testicles. So he was no doctor. But again it was the year 610. No one had much of a clue how the human body worked but he did love to make stuff up."

God pauses and you can see him thinking. A smile crosses his faces. He lets out a blast of laughter.

"All daughters! Ha-ha-ha-ha! There's some Karma for you."

"What about the 72 virgins you get when you die? I hear that one all the time"

"A surprise to you Western world sorts, The Qur'an does not say anything about 72 virgins. Mohammad would tell his Arab soldiers that if they died fighting for him, he would score them the 72 virgins in a physical heaven, next to Allah. Extremists still believe this today: Again with the sex and virgins. That is so such a guy thing and a

wrong thing. Here is the other thing: I am Allah. Could you see heaven, near my golden throne with 72 virgins for every Muslin soldier clipped? It would be a very inexperienced whore house; that heaven. And where do you find that many virgins? Not on this planet."

Mr. Funny God.

"Why were you whispering?"

"There are Christian and Muslim fanatics who would rather see Me dead than tell you what I just told you."

"I don't see anyone here now."

"When you go around like I do talking about the truth, those boys get a little cranky. Muslins and Jews, but especially the lunatic Christians are the worst. Sometimes it's safer to speak looking like a homeless nut than looking like a high priest. I try to save myself the confrontation until I am done."

"Done?"

"Talking to you. We need to make sure we finish."

That sounds odd. There was an uneasiness about what God just said; like he knew what was around the corner for him and, and … me? I decide to live in the moment and dismiss the uncomfortable reference to time.

"What about the Mormons?"

God stops laughing and rolls his eyes, and exhales..

"They don't get it, either. Those boys started around 1830 and they believe Joseph Smith was elevated by God to straighten out the church of God that was abandoned by Christians. This one should give you a level of reality of the Mormons as a religion to be taken seriously; they wouldn't allow black priests until 1978. Do we need to go any further? You can lump those boys into the same racist pile of narrow thinkers with the others not allowing women to be priests or rabbis to this day. I think women are lucky that they don't have to deal with the nonsense. Let the boys have their elitist, social club,

211

disguised as religion, while the woman enjoy being the true center of religion, unconditionally baring, raising, and loving their children."

I'm learning that religion blows.

28

Truth be told, I thought I looked a lot like Jay Z
when I was on earth with the name Jesus.

I walk over to The Bible and start feathering through
some of the pages. Each page felt like it weighed a couple pounds.
It was an illustrated Bible, with bright, large, letters in script
writing and large illustrations on nearly every page. I think it was
printed for children or young teenagers consumption.

On many of the pages there are pictures of Christ on
Earth: a highlight reel of the teachings in The Bible and
illustrations for each of the big events and miracles. The guy now
sitting at the table behind me wearing a woman's gym shoe,
prominently propped up on one end of the table crossed over a
tongue-less army boot, is God and doesn't look remotely like this
guy in here.

"Did you look like this?"

God gets up and groans, walks over right behind me,
and peers over my shoulder at the illustration of Christ praying in

213

the Garden of Gethsemane. The photo shows a lily white man with light blondish, brown hair, crystal blue eyes, and, of course, a white robe and yellow halo around his head.

"Nah, I was light-skinned, but much closer to black, with jet-black hair at the time. Just about everyone back then was very dark. Truth be told, I thought I looked a lot like Jay Z when I was on earth with the name Jesus."

"The rapper?"

God responds a bit confrontationally.

"Yes, the rapper! I saw him on television. He was sitting in the stands watching a basketball game; the Nets of New Jersey were playing the male deers from Milwaukee."

"The Bucks."

"What?"

"The… never mind."

"I thought his skin tone looked just like mine. Now the television was not good so I might have been darker, but for sure I had the flat, wider nose, skinny face, and larger ears. I saw him on a music video, and it startled me how much we looked alike. I spent weeks picking through Dumpsters looking for the sunglasses like the ones he wore in a music video I saw. The rich and warm cocoa brown color with shiny, black hair with that wonderful tight curl is a fantastic and handsome look. I loved it. It was a great gene mix back then. I was taller than most, too, lanky. You got something against rap?"

"No, just never followed it much, so I don't know how he looks."

"You should follow it. It is the sound and the voice of the spirit and the soul. You need to listen. Humanity needs to listen to rap, or to any voice crying out. When society screams out, in pain, love should surround it, nurture it, protect it, heal it, and then grow the love together as one, easing the pain, spreading the love. Sure, some rap is crap, the gang banging stuff to sell records, but don't lump, listen. They are today's disciples, town criers, poets of a suppressed brother. Humanity should listen to all the cries of pain; humanity should dry all the tears, seek out the fire that burns in society's soul, and extinguish it. But instead it is easier to ignore pain and build walls."

"You don't look like Jay Z in any of these renderings in this Bible. What happened?"

"I got white when the God road show went to the western Mediterranean through the Roman Empire. Those crazy Romans couldn't have God being a brother. And just so you know God, I, did not make this Christ in the image of man like it says here in the book. That guy-"

He points to the illustration.

"-there, was created by the first Roman Emperor, the one who was the first one to believe in Christianity."

"Who was that?"

"You don't follow your history?"

"Do you have to be so critical? I'm just trying to keep up. I'm trying to keep this together. This is all moving a little fast for me, … and whatever I have left in the tank from my wife's death has been just about emptied by you, so please, cut me some fucking slack."

He paused, nodded in agreement.

"My bad. It was Constantine the First. He ruled Rome around…"

You could see him actually trying to remember, rolodexing through his centuries of memories. He was tapping his forehead with the shortened ring finger on his left hand. Odd looking? Yes, but no longer startling to me. God, God was fascinating.

"… around the year 325 C.E. after my death as Jesus. He was the first Roman ruler to allow people to worship as Christians. He allowed the building of churches and public worship. He was also a nut."

"A nut?"

"Well, besides running the Roman Empire for 20 years, he created the white Christ. He didn't like me looking black. So he combined the image of his son's face and his wife's

215

eyes. He created the image you see throughout the books today. He said he wanted to create an image of a strong Christ with loving eyes. Both his wife and his son were spoiled, fat, and poorly educated, and Constantine eventually had them both killed; Father of the Year! The image of me? He had an artist create the god-likeness you are all praying to today. Any artistic renderings of me prior to that time were ordered destroyed, but there weren't many. That's how I became white."

"That truly blows."

"Don't sweat it. Get past the color thing as quickly as you can. It will broaden your world. By the way, it could have been worse. The king could have not had any children, and portrayed me as one of his many large Rottweiler's. You all would be praying to a dog-man with a bad attitude, so chin up."

God can be a funny guy sometimes. He knew I needed a little light humor.

We walk away from The Bible over to a quieter area of the library and find one of those large, library tables you can hardly reach across. He sat on one side and motions me to take a seat on the other. It then dawned on me the last time I was sitting at one of these large library tables: It was a night in college, at the university library, when my wife and I told each other for the first time, that we loved each other. God watches a small grin cross my lips. I say nothing.

"Come here. Let me help you with that."

He extends his hand across the table. I put mine in his. He firmly grasps it. In an instant I am taken back to the moment: the feeling, the smell, the embrace, her voice of the night in the library back at our University. Pow! He lets' go and the feeling, the emotion passes. A moment of shock, surprise, and bliss; it is addictive.

"Thank you"

"You're welcome. I was getting cynical back there, and when I talk about a lot of these things I have a tendency to blame the people I happen to be speaking to. My bad. Now,

do you want to spend what could be days blowing holes in The Bible or would you like to know the truth, the true miracles of the universe and here on earth?"

      I am still getting over the euphoric fix of being with my wife in that library. I have been catapulted into a great mood. .

"I'm ready."

      I reset my brain and adjust my ass on the hard wooden chair; making it creek.

"So the library has the teachings?"

"Not so much teachings, but truths about the earth and the universe: my little miracles. And these truths I speak of have not been locked away for centuries, written on some secret parchment and rolled into holy scrolls. To the contrary, it has been just the last hundred years or so and in some cases the last ten or twenty years in which wiser people have been figuring out what those miracles actually are. Today's brightest thinkers - your scientists, chemists, biologists, astronomers, and philosophers-"

"…like Einstein?"

"- are starting to get it right, and are putting their arms and minds around the miracles of the universe. These are the true miracles of God. Those are the disciples who speak the truth."

"Most of those guys don't believe in a supreme being. Most scientists are atheists."

"Actually that is not the case at all. What they don't believe in is The Bible and the explanation of how creation happened. If, or when, the bright guys figure out there is a conscious attachment to the science of the universe and that attachment has been misconstrued as religion for the last 6,000 years, they will be the ones leading people to the truth about the universe, evolution, and the power of love. Churches will become extension of universities of higher learning. It will be your next golden era of awareness and evolution."

"Are you seeing the future?"

217

"No, it's just the process of the developing mind and the human spirit, and... I've watched it happen before."

"It's starting here much slower than I expected. I thought Einstein would have been the break-through guy, but I was wrong. He struggled with it. After his papers on the universe were published, he tried rewriting them a number of times. He was vexed with the idea of what I had showed him. He knew I was right, but he didn't have the nerve to publish it. Check the records. After "Energy" came out he did virtually nothing. I look back and think I may have been too excited to think a human had finally evolved to 'get it.' I was probably wrong to show him. HE was so certain of his line of thinking, his educated, internal instincts would not allow him to accept the truth."

God goes all melancholy on me. You could tell he thought he failed. I try to pep him up.

"Chin up! Come on! Let's get what we came for: How about a few miracles and these heroes you speak of who stuck to their guns!"

God scratches his crotch, snorts, sneezes, then clears his throat. Is he about to hocka loogie? It wouldn't surprise me.

"You're right! That's what we came for. Let's talk miracles, and then let's get something to eat."

"Great idea, but not Moe's! It'll be my treat!"

29

But let's back up to a little time before the Big Bang.

I have rekindled his enthusiasm. He must really be hungry. I figure we have an hour before the library closes. I sit in amazement. Not at the fact that a person that sleeps on the street, eats from a Dumpster, has a collapsed lung, and speaks like a nuclear physicist is God and about to tell me the secrets of the universe. No, the amazing thing is that I believe him.

"What miracles should we start with?"

"Well, let me begin by clarifying the word miracles."

"This isn't going to be one of those, 'the word miracle actually means mayonnaise or something, like the word love thing to you describes energy of the universe' and to me it means 'a school boy crush' or something confusing like that, is it?"

"Yuck, yuck, Mr. Smarty Pants. Here it is. Up until this moment when people describe something truly amazing and do not know how it happens, the word miracle seems to crop up in the explanation. Back in the old days, there were plenty more miracles than there are today, just because today you can explain things more rationally, scientifically. Humans have gotten smarter, so there is less need to call everything a miracle. Horrible,

mostly unexplained things are acts of God, and unexplained cool things are miracles. Truth be known: God doesn't do parlor tricks. The expanding universe writes the history. That's what makes this journey so great - it's on auto pilot."

"Got it."

"Right. Everything that happens that is not controlled by people is just the natural process of a living universe. This universe is big and alive and like anything that is alive, it has byproducts, entrails, collateral damage - but none of it is planned. So miracles to me are a few very cool things that have been created in the universe, but it's not like I was sitting around thinking about cool things to create or changing water into wine."

"So what you are saying is that you don't do miracles, but the universe you created has parts of it that, in your opinion, are really cool and should be mentioned or described as a miraculous."

"For the sake of getting to dinner, let me just say that that is pretty close. The first truly amazing event worth calling a miracle was the creation of the universe."

"We talked about the Big Bang."

"Well let's back up to a little time before your Big Bang."

"What? Before what? Before everything that is …was?"

"Why do you think that?"

"I just thought, I just thought it was the beginning of it all. Wasn't it?"

"It was the beginning of it all based on what you all invented or guessed. Someone had to throw the switch."

Dead uncomprehending silence. My brain just turned to seaweed.

"So there was a before?"

"Yes! We got a winner! You bet there was. You want the simple version or the complex version?"

220

"Instead of me trying to formulate a somewhat intelligent question, could you save me the embarrassment and tell me what was before and how the universe came to be in the simple version?"

"Sure. We need to go back a few hours to when I explained to you how I describe your evolution and the energy of the universe…"

"…love."

"…yes, love. The love you possess and the love you gather from others, as we learned from our friend Albert Einstein, EVOLVES back into energy just like atoms, and on Earth, just like carbon. And what Al did not share with the world after I distinctly told him to do so, was to explain to the world that this energy, when evolved from you, is thinking, processing energy. It is aware. It is you, it is me, it is our souls; it is we. Allow me to digress fifteen billion years ago."

"There is this man, for a lack of a better term you can comprehend, not from this universe, who is loved by many, many millions of people, and he shares this love with all thinking life forms on his home planet and millions of other planets beyond his own. He is so advanced he learns how to combine conscious love with the energy of the universe all around him."

God gets to his feet. His voice increases in volume and urgency. He doesn't mind people hearing this part. His excitement grows.

"When this man eventually evolves, his energy is vast, so strong, so powerful that it, to put it simply, virtually out- runs the expanding universe he was a part of. And with the energy he possesses, creates, blows up, bangs, whatever you wish to call it, yes, creates a new universe! This new universe is the universe you presently inhabit."

What the fuck. Again, I am dumbfounded. I sit here with this stupid look on my face. I am numb. I can't even come close to getting this - and this was the simple version? I sit here throbbing with ignorance. I am a speck of nothing compared to this, this, this man, this God - my God! I try to form a sentence to respond, but my lips are stuck to my teeth and I can't swallow. I got nothing. God is just standing there, arms straight out at his side, Christ-on-a-cross like. Oh God! And then it dawns on me. I fly to my feet! I raise my hand and wave my index finger at him.

221

"That person, that person was, was, was, you? You are our God! You are our God of our universe."

"Duh!"

"You were just a regular guy on some planet that people … people?... people loved, and loved, and loved some more, and you evolved into the ultimate power in the universe, so big that you blew the lid off the joint and created this universe. It was you! You are my GOD OF MY UNIVERSE!"

"I have said that no fewer than 50 times in the last two days."

I fall back into my chair, numb with trying to process and, I am at a loss for words. I think I just crossed over to a place where I am having trouble connecting the dots. It all just got too big. I feel a feverish blush roll up my neck and around to my cheeks. I am light-headed. I feel really small and stupid.

"You okay?"

I nod yes but inside I know I'm not. God, is this truly God, the supreme being of my universe.

"You sure you're okay? Well, I just thought now that you know how it all started, for YOU, you'll see that it's a cycle of love, or energy, which-ever you can handle better right now. Are you sure you are okay?"

Fuck no, I'm not okay.

"Yeah, I'm okay."

I lie.

"Okay, so the love grows, and as you now know, that love is energy, and then when it gets big enough, strong enough, powerful enough, it separates, it expands."

"You mean it replicated, like cell division, separating into two?"

"Wow, Albert Einstein has nothing on you. You're getting it. We are all on this ever growing, ever evolving, ever expanding cycle of energy, as small as human cell division and all the way up to the very large cell division of the universe: growing, separating, and growing again. And before it dawns on you to ask…"

Big pause. He sits down and leans in to whisper.

"There is no other God above me in this universe. So don't make up shit if you are going to write anything. I am as supreme as it gets. I have no father cycling in a universe that encompasses this one. So holster the sci-fi, creative, religious, and assumptive bullshit."

"Have you ever told anyone about how it works or worked?"

God shakes his head in mock frustration with a sarcastic smile.

"Of course! I have told scads of people: you, Einstein, anyone who would listen to me. Where do you think they get the stories in that stupid book? I tell them what I just told you!"

He again flings his arm toward the section where The Bible rests in its wooden cradle.

"Throughout generations I have sat with people and shared the same exact stories. Just think what you know about The Bible now and the guys who wrote it. I told those guys exactly, EXACTLY, what I told you. Now, you want to re-read the book of Genesis? They wrote Genesis based on what I just told you. The best description they could fathom about what I just said to you was God created the universe and the world in seven days. They dumbed it down for the masses but it was the best they could do."

"Oh my… and the story of Christ …"

"Me!…"

"…you, on earth, then ascend into heaven to become the son of God?"

"They just got it all confused. When I was on earth as Jesus, over 2000 years ago, I laid it out the same way. I told them that I was regular guy who was loved by many, and when I evolved, the energy of the love I had allowed me punch a hole in my universe and create a new universe, their universe. How they wrote it didn't come out the way I told

223

them. I told them just how I told you and you got The passion. They painted me into a man, and then I got clipped - ah crucified - and then they took off with the idea of me running the universe as God. They threw in the God title and the died-for-our-sins thing so all my followers wouldn't revolt. The rulers wanted me gone so I didn't take over their kingdoms..."

"Herod?"

"Yes, said that he was just following my orders and was part of my plan so he wasn't killed. Then they feathered in the 'died for our sins' to make my murder a righteous act for the people to be saved by me. What a crock of shit. But it stuck."

"Why did they write that you would come back to judge. You didn't tell them that did you?"

"What I said was...."

God clears his throat and waves his short finger at me.

"I come back all the time to visit. I like coming back. I like to check in on things on occasion. I love to visit and speak and watch people, people that may need some help, who need to learn about, or re-learn about love, and how to grow love. The guys that killed Jesus; me, and the high priests that were part of the present political machine made up the judging thing so everyone would fear me and stay under the tight grasp of the present rulers; utter bull shit."

"Wow that information will sure screw up religion."

"And it should. It's all not true. I come here to help you and others; but I have been here so many times. When I mentioned to them that I come back, they wrote it as I was coming back to judge everyone, send them either to heaven or hell. That was one of the reasons I never came back to the people I met before or came back to the same place or with the same looks or immediately after my death. Where do they get this crap? I only spoke of love and they make up heaven and hell and judgment. I give them an A for interesting shit, but there's no truth there."

"So you got strong with love and boom! The Big Bang?"

"Within a New York second, too swift to explain with words, my energy produced the universe and all the forces that govern physics. How's your science?"

224

I gave him my best "I am not a dumb-ass" look. He didn't buy it.

"I'll go slowly. The energy level now is enormous. In less than a minute the universe is a million billion miles across, and growing. Plus it is over ten billion degrees. It's essentially a very large nuclear reaction creating the lighter elements - principally hydrogen, and helium, and a little bit of lithium. Within three minutes all matter that will ever exist in this universe has been produced; made it all in the time it takes to make your bed. It is a closed circuit. Whatever we have at the inception is all we will have."

"And you said earlier it happened?...."

"Some bright people think it was 13.5 or 13.6 billion, but it actually is a more. We've been around for a while."

"Why the difference between what scientists believe and what the actual time was?"

"Hold on, that's not that bad of an estimate. You guys are getting really close. For centuries you had no clue."

"What did we do to start figuring it out?"

"You built the Hubble telescope, put it on a rocket and sent it into space. Right now you are learning that the Hubble has become the constant in all new equations. Since it is real math and not philosophy, you are looking at actual data for the first time, enabling you to get close to correctly calculating the age of the universe based on the speed of its expansion."

"So the books are off a little?"

"Yep, the miscalculation is written over there, two rows over, at the end of the aisle under 'SPACE EXPLORATION. Why they put it there, I don't know, probably because NASA shot the Hubble up and gave the scientist the info to measure the distance stuff is moving away from us. What is cool now is that you are starting to get your hands around the physics of what happened, and the closer you get your hands around the science, the quicker you will eventually get to the truth about energy, the power of love, where you are going, what your part is in the grand scheme and when you are going to get there. It won't be in your time, but life as you know it on Earth will be friendly and

loving. No wars or conflicts, people will reach to others with love, there will be no boundaries. I am excited about now, this time in history, because the real truth is starting to peek its head out of the fantasy world you are all living in. It's exciting for me to see."

"Who was the first to discover it?"

"The start of the universe?"

"Yeah."

"Theories began to crop up in the late 1800s. Check out the Frenchman Henri Poincare. He was on to it. Even Darwin in the 1700s was getting it, but it was embraced when Einstein had the clout to put it all together and sell it. I just helped Einstein fill in the details, and that's when everybody in the religions tried to blow holes into it. They couldn't, and slowly the scholars started looking more like the people with the truth and the religions more like the people preaching fantasy. The real fun started when it went from theory to reality; proof."

"When was that?"

"Back in 1965, Arno Penzias and Robert Wilson in Holmdel, New Jersey, over there in the periodicals no one ever reads, were trying to make use of a large communications antenna, but they were getting all kinds of static, and for the life of them they couldn't get rid of it. So they contacted Robert Dicke at Princeton University, 30 miles away, and explained that wherever they pointed this large communications antenna, anywhere in the sky, they would get this static. What those two boys had discovered and what Dicke affirmed was that they were hearing the edge of the universe still banging away, still growing, still expanding. All of a sudden, after that everything got real. You really want to find out about the big bang, build the Superconducting super collider. You will get your answers. No more dismissing things as chariots in the sky or old wives' tales or aliens - this was the real deal, the actual proof that the expanding universe theory was not a theory but is still happening. Some Energy in action. Love in action!"

"Not to be doom and gloomy, but how long will our sun last?"

"There's no plan. Sorry, but based on the history, size, and when your sun was created, you have 4.5 billion years to get your faculties in order then the party really starts. Your sun does not have the mass to become a super nova. It will throw off its outer layer, forming a nebula. Then it will slowly cool and then fade."

"Can you stop it!"

"No, and by then you won't want to, either. Four and a half billion years is a long time, and that's 4.5 billion years if nothing runs into Earth. The universe is vast, but gravity adds an interesting element to the game. You will probably get cracked by something like a meteor before the sun turns off. You also should know your present sun was not the first but the third."

"Really?"

"The universe is a big place. Don't sweat it. Also, I keep reminding you of the level of your intelligence now and your intelligence in the future. It's like comparing your present intellect to the first up-right humans six million years ago: Orrorin tugenensis."

"A roarin' wha-?"

"Does it really matter?

"Come on."

"They were the first, upright, walking humans; bipedalism. Scientists still argue that they may not be the first, but they were. Their only point of reference is a femur found in northwest Kenya. Just west of Kenya there is a lake named Lake Victoria. It is the largest lake in Africa. It is shared by Kenya, Tanzania, and Uganda. If they go to the west shore in Uganda, in the village of Lukaya, and dig there, they will find definitive proof of what they are looking for. You would be amazed how far you will come from shit fights and foraging for foliage around the fire at Lake Victoria to now. You as a race will adapt and eventually exercise that keen intellect. Your existence won't be like it is now. You will develop the ability to travel from different evolutional and mental plains of existence while you are still human and if I may say…breathing."

"You lost me."

"Remember that thing I just showed you when I held onto you and we became part of the energy of the universe? You got all wet?"

"Oh shit yeah! Breathe! Of course, I'm still drying out."

"Imagine people having or I should say learning, sharing, and earning the ability to evolve to higher plain of existence, like you did through harnessing the universe's energy.

This will not be your final development or the end of your human existence, but it will be like what happened with me when we went for that ride and then came back to your human state."

"Are you saying that what I just experienced with your help... people will be able to do that without holding onto God?"

"Yes! Do you really think you will travel through the galaxy in your human state, as you are now propelled fast enough to get anywhere? Do you really think humans can build something on Earth that will shoot them through space fast enough to reach some other place without taking hundreds of years to get there? No way! They will evolve their intellectual assets and start dismissing the concept of strapping themselves to a can of gasoline and lighting it like you all have been doing with your NASA program - interesting, but infantile. When you grow..."

He taps his forehead referencing the human race's brain.

"...you will harness the energy of love in your hearts and souls, couple it with that of others and have the ability to freely move through the universe. That is why when the sun finally runs out of fuel humans will probably have evolved well beyond the meager ability you have today and become citizens of the expanding universe. You will be very different bipedal boy."

"How big is our galaxy or the solar system?"

"Are we really going to do science class?"

"You said I could ask anything."

"Alright. In light years the galaxy is a million times a million times a million light years wide and expanding."

"And the solar system?"

"What confuses people is the way you show it in your school books."

"What do you mean?"

"Well, you know how in science books they show the solar system with planets circling out from the sun: Mercury then Venus, then Earth, and on, and on, and they all seem comfortably similar distances from each other?"

"Yeah"

"Actually, if the Earth were the size of a pea here in my hand…"

God holds his hand cupped.

"… Jupiter would be over a 1,000 feet away. The nearest star other than the sun from this pea would be 10,000 miles away. This is just the galaxy we are in. Tonight when you see the North Star sparkle, that sparkle occurred 680 years ago, and it took that long to get here at the speed of light."

"So the galaxy and solar system are really big."

"Big to you now."

30

I guess to them you are aliens.

"Let's move on. How old is the planet Earth?"

"Four point six billion years ago, right where we are now, a great swirl of gas 15 billion miles across accumulated. Most of the gases, roughly 99%, were used to create the sun. In the process a few tiny specks of dust got close enough to gravitate to one another, then more and more and more dust and space specks accumulated into a rock then a boulder, on and on. The bigger it got the more gravity it possessed, which means more galactic dust was drawn to the Earth. And in a blink of an eye..."

"How long?"

".....in 200 million years..."

"Some blink."

"... the Earth was created."

"Not 6 days?"

"Six days? Oh Genesis, Old Testament. Nope, not six days. And remember, Genesis actually said I created the entire universe in six days not just the Earth".

"What about the moon?"

"Oh, you'll like this. A planet the size of Mars crashed into the Earth. Think about that for a minute."

"That must have been something to see."

"Yeah, it was, from a distance. A huge chunk of the Earth's crust broke off and started circling the Earth collecting its space dust and eventually creating the moon."

"Really?"

"That theory was created by Reginald Daley of Harvard."

He points to shelves over his left shoulder.

"...two rows over, third shelf on the aisle marked, 'Nobody reads this shit anymore. Old Reggie was right and it was verified by Neil Armstrong after they spent all that time and money to go see if the moon was made of cheese, only to get there they found out it was made of Earth. They had kind of figured that before anyways. Bright dudes."
"How much does the earth weigh?"

"Ask Henri Cavendish, four rows over, first shelf, a scientist from London, England. In 1797 he figured out it weighed in at 5.92725 billion trillion metric tons."

"Did you tell him how much it weighs? Back then?"

"No, I didn't tell him. Hell, I didn't know! He just figured it out."

God seems to be falling into an attitude of a bored, carnival, magic answer-man. I get the impression he has answered these questions a few times before and I wish I had my fifth grade teacher Mrs. Cordier with me now. She would have peppered God with good questions. She knew everything and she was tough. I know she would not have been nervous.

"Okay, give me a true miracle."

"Four hundred million years ago, on this planet, you crawled out from the sea and began to breathe air. That may not sound like too big of a miracle to a guy like you who has been breathing air all his life but air, oxygen, is combustible, and all your foods derived

from manganese, selium and zinc are poisonous everywhere else in the universe except for here. That information is over there in the section marked 'EARTH SCIENCE'. Your evolution is truly the second biggest miracle in the history of your existence thus far."

"So there are aliens?"

"Depends on whose perspective you are looking at it from. I guess to them you are aliens. But all species are similar in many ways, yet still different. It's all based on their surroundings. How far away from their sun or energy source are they? What is the chemical composition of their planet? How the soup was stirred up. All that makes up a species is based on the way the universe deals the cards to a certain planet. That determines how the species evolves and how they survive, live, and grow."

"Take the Earth for instance; if the earth were a couple hundred miles further from the sun, you would not be here. If the chemical composition is a little different, you all don't crawl out of the water and evolve to thinking humans; you stay pond scum. There are two constants everywhere: you will or will not evolve based on the chemistry of your planet if it is chemically meant to be, but - and this is really important: all intelligent life, in the universe, loves."

"How are we similar to aliens? I mean, other species in the universe?"

"I am not going to describe the physicality of a species! Damn, you humans here get stuck on the wrapping paper and not the gift. Curious, simple minded species."

"Chill, man! I'm just a *Star Trek* and *Star Wars* fan!"

"Sorry. But know this: every advanced species in the universe, as you are slowly becoming, evolves to higher levels like you will when your soul and spirit evolve. You want to meet new friends? Wait until you evolve. But when you do, you won't see any difference in one spirit from another. I am sure that disappoints you, Mr. Sulu."

Funny God.

"I always thought other species would be much more advanced, like in the movies."

"Some are. Most are within a billion years' time of your growth. Imagine the bang continuing to ripple out. This means that your neighbors in surrounding solar systems are

on your same growth and development curve or time line. So unlike the science fiction movies on television; you are all about on the same pace of your intellectual evolution."

"Could there be a hostile inter-stellar encounter?

"Yes."

"Have there been hostile inter-stellar encounters?"

"Yes. It is nothing different than one country here on Earth attacking another; just a bigger Stratego board. But the rules of the expanding universe, free will and love apply. And if you hate on a galactic level your evolution, well, I can't even imagine".

"Will we ever hook up with the aliens?"

"Aliens?"

"Sorry, other species?"

"Yes, unless you blow yourselves up before you can continue to evolve. Let's go eat. I am hungry."

"Well, hold on. I'm just starting to get this. It is starting to make sense. As big as the universe is, and as small as we are, we are all connected...to everything...everywhere."

"Yes. I am really hungry."

"One more miracle please."

"We've got to go. I want to eat something and the library is about to close.

31

*Take him now, or they will kill him right here
right now, and they will not stop com -*

I can tell God is really hungry and not just complaining.
He has taken his now empty, jacket pocket where he shoved the
half hamburger and fries earlier, and turned the pocket inside-out
licking and sucking it. He knows how to make his point and get
his way. We both stand. I stretch while he sucks his coat. I feel as
if I just finished a final exam in college. My brain is newly packed
with an enormous amount of information. I wish I had recorded
it or written it down. The guy who delivered the information
doesn't seem as mentally fatigued, just hungry. His attention is
consumed by a big glob of dried ketchup mixed with lint.

I, clear my throat, God gets the idea that watching him
sucking on his coat is disturbing me. He jerks his coat back down
to his waist and tucks his pocket back in. He pulls his hand out
and sucks the finger-tips. His hand is dark with dirt but his finger-
tips are clean from sucking them - except for under his fingernails,
they are black.

As we slowly walk down the stairs this time, not
speaking, the lights are being turned out behind us and the sounds
of chains being slung around aluminum door handles make us
both quicken our pace to insure we are not forgotten and locked

inside. It sounds haunting and sad. The wealth of knowledge that answers so many questions in our universe is locked away at a place that no one visits anymore. I know - the internet - but there is something collegiate, scholastic and inspiring, about being in a library. The possibility of discovery draws your curiosity. Staring into a screen-saver of your dog just doesn't carry the same impact.

As we hurry out, reaching the main entry-way, God looks back at the only person I see in the main foyer: a woman who looks to be a 100 years old. She is transfixed on him as he leaves. I watch her watching him. He passes out the double doors first. As he disappears from her view, I slow to watch her. She bows her head and makes the sign of the cross: right hand, forehead to stomach, then left breast to right. She then kisses her half clenched fist, looks at me and nods, and turns away. She knows. She knows who he is.

Because of my curiosity about of this woman, I am now three full strides behind God as he makes his way through the heavy, wooden, outer double doors. As I push the second door open to the outside that has already closed in front of me, I am met with an eerie sight. In the twilight of the early evening there are no fewer than 500 people standing in front of the library and in the park across the street, riveted to God as he exits the building. I have never had to judge the size of a crowd, but it seemed like thousands to me.

God stands frozen on the library stoop. He smiles. There is a silence, an odd anticipation to the motionless crowd; but for what? Will there be fireworks? Will there be singing? No, nothing that fancy but something much more fascinating. One person close to the front kneels and thrusts his hands toward God. The throng follows suit. God shakes his head and motions with his hands and arms to stand-up, put their hands down and hold hands.

Beginning in the front of the crowd and connecting throughout the throng, a human chain is formed, finally ending with a young child, mother's hand in his. He then extends his right hand up and out to God. How do they all know my God is God? Fuck. Odd. He looks over to me.

"Not odd. I have been working your neighborhood for a while."

My mind-reading, smart-ass God reaches for the little person's hand and holds it gently. He then reaches back and grabs my hand. I follow his lead and hold the hand of an old man standing next to me whose hand was extended out to mine. In that very instant when all our hands are joined, there is a warm joyful satisfaction, an attitude, a smile, "love" that comfortably cycles through us all. Not the intense levels of energy rush I shared with God inside the library, but more the feeling of a hug from a favorite grandmother or mom. I glance at faces throughout the crowd. All were smiling, all were at ease, and all were perfectly comfortable and satisfied. God spends another few seconds with the crowd and with a very large smile looks back at me.

"We are in grave danger. You shouldn't be close to me now."

"What? What the fuck? What did you say?"

"Go now! You must leave now!"

I am shocked, surprised.

"What's wrong? What the fuck is wrong?"

"There are people here who want to harm me. And if they know you are with me, they will harm you. Go!"

"No! No, fuck no! I won't. Let me find a cop!"

"It won't matter."

"Who's going to harm you?"

"It doesn't matter who. Go!"

"No Goddamn it, who?"

"Funny, Goddamn it. There are many that want to harm me, and I believe they are out there now. I can feel them. Please, please go!"

"No!"

      The crowd begins to move a bit. The feeling of love is being replaced by a tremor of shallow anxiety that spreads through the crowd. I can sense it too. The odd thing about the energy of love is that once you know the feeling, you are also keenly aware of the feeling of hate or the void when love disappears. The hate starts rocketing through the crowd as quickly as the love did. This is what God was feeling and so were some of the more keenly aware people in the throng.

"Please go! We will talk later."

"No fuckin' way, I will not leave you."

      I muster up the courage I thought I had lost when my wife died. But without hesitation, I leave my place by God's side and stand directly in front of him, now separating him from the crowd and obscuring the crowd's ability to see him. I peer into the crowd, looking for what? Danger? Guys in black hats? I am way out of my comfort zone, but it feels exhilarating. Within seconds, 11 other people follow suit, creating a human shield around God. One of the 11 who came to protect God pulls a lazar gadget from his pocket and points it directly at God. God's gorgeous blue eyes turn yellow, his face is awash with a night-vision, green hue. Fuck me! The little fucker is painting God as a target. Who the fuck are these people?

      I break ranks, take five big strides and I am on the fucker. I drive my face right into the cock-suckers chest. Stay low, drive through the body. Thanks Coach! I jerk my head up and head butt his chin. The motherfucker howls. The laser pointer was not a pointer at all, but some real military hardware. When we hit the ground I crush the fuck, ribs cracking air presses from his slight build. The lazar targeting device flies from his hand and falls into the crowd. I quickly get to my feet. Kick the fucker in the side of his head and retreat back in front of God. God looks at me with a wide smile, laughing.

"Don't kick anyone in the head. It really hurts."

"What? Fuck'em, I got to take care of you!"

"Who are you? What happened to my sad little friend?"

"Your friend's getting his game back."

I pound my heart. God nods at me with a smile. Tension replaces serenity throughout the crowd. I don't care, I am frosty. A scuffle in the back of the crowd sends everyone scrambling in all directions in a frenzied panic. I hear shrieks. The word 'Gun!' cuts through the chilly air. Screams replace silence; hate replaces love. In the moment it takes for a heart to beat or a cell to split into two, I hear the whistle of something passing close to my right ear. The wall behind me explodes into concrete rubble: Then it happens again! We are being shot at!

"God!"

I glance at God. He is calm, serene, emotionally out of place - and still standing! The moment turns surreal for me, car wreck in slow motion. My ears begin to burn. My throat swells. I cannot breathe. God begins to raise his arms out from his sides giving whoever is shooting at him a bigger target.

"Stop that! Put your fucking arms down!"

I grab both his arms and slam them against his sides. Cold and darkness of hate rushes up my spine. I become dizzy and nauseated. Who are these fuckers? I want their asses in a bag! Rage blankets my fear. My legs and arms are Jell-O wobbling. I struggle for sure footing. Adrenaline, no, battery fucking acid, pumps through my veins. If the pricks who want to fuck with my God were close enough, I would bite out their larynxes. With the second bite, I would tear their jugulars from their necks while I hold their heads in place, in a bowling ball grip. Index finger through the left eye socket; fuck you finger through the right - all comfortably gliding on the gelatinous remains of their eyeballs. For pure sporting satisfaction I would bite off their fucking noses so their mother's would have to look at a closed casket. Fuck-em! I am now pure hate. I feel shallow, lonely, dirty, ugly, and inhumane. I want to kill something. God fires a hard stare at me and shakes his head no.

"That's not what we do!"

And at that moment, it dawns on me; within two minutes I have felt the apex of the emotional pendulum swing from love to hate. Love is pure. Hate is a contagious cancer. Fuck it! We need to get him out of harm's way. I knock God to the ground and try to cover him.

I feel or hear, I don't know, the odd sensation of bullets passing by again. I thought they always made big, gunshot noises, Spaghetti Western style. But no; there is not the big bang and ricochet sound, just a little cracking noise in the middle of the screams. All I hear is pop, sizzling air, then an explosion of concrete above my head all sharing the same split second of time. The mortar rains down on my shoulders and back as we now crouch down low under a pile of fallen humanity.

A man who had rushed up to the stoop to help is now slumped over on God's left side, I am on God's right. In the middle of the hail of concrete and screams, the man looks directly into my eyes and firmly says,

"Take him now or they will kill him right here, right now, and they will not stop com-."

There is no breath left to form his last word. He is silent. His head falls over to his right shoulder. The left side of his face has been obliterated by the exit wound of a bullet. Blood and chunks of bone and flesh slide off what remains of the front part of his skull and clumps into the crevasse between his neck and his clerical collar. I see his rosary slip from his hand and land in a pool of his own blood, lots of it.

For reasons I can't explain, I try to pick up the rosary, but in the cool of the evening the blood is quickly becoming tacky or slippery, shit, I don't know, it's just hard to pick it up, but I finally do and knot it around his wrist, also soaked in blood. I press the cross into his dead hand. His body seems to have doubled in weight, limp as it slumps against us. I reach up and close his eyelids over his now hollow eyes, and gingerly push his body out of our way. He lays pooled in his own blood. Blood looks black in the dark. There is so much blood. I thought God may have been shot. I scream to him:

"God!"

Calmly.

"What?"

"We've got to get out of here…now!"

I grab him by the scruff of his coat, take two large strides toward the side of the porch, shoes covered in blood, I slip, stumble, fall, and barrel roll to the edge of the porch with God still in my grasp. As Newton's first law of motion states: things that are in motion tend to stay in motion, and we were in motion; aisle two, second shelf, under NATURAL THEORISTS AND PHILOSOPHERS.

We roll off the porch and fall four feet into the crotch of the building where the porch and facade meet. Our landing is slightly cushioned by a half-dead hedge, then we come to rest behind it. God is directly on top of me, both of us soaked in blood. We are now out of sight, I think. I fling him off my chest against the wall. The shots don't seem to be following us.

"We've got to get you the fuck out of here!"

"No, I think it's time."

"Time? Time for what?"

240

It dawns on me: He believes that this is the time he is supposed to die, yet again.

"No, it is *not* time! Not now! Let's move!"

This time, when we get up to move, he seems leaning more toward survival and he is not as keen in ending it here. He glances at me and smiles. I think he is actually is trying to get away now just to make me feel better or another test to measure my heeling.

Sirens replace the gun-shots. Screams are replaced with howls of agony as family members kneel over dead loved ones. We run low, hunched over, our heads down. We get to the corner of the building, turn left, and continue down the alley. My adrenalin is pumping. We are running full speed, my hand still clenching the back of God's collar.

32

Religious people? Religious people want to kill you?

We are two blocks down the alley and God slows to a trot, then a walk. I try to make him keep running by tugging his collar, but he stops, the jacket flops over his head, and then we both are stopped, both trying to catch our breath.

"Come on!"

"We're far enough away! They're gone!"

"What the fuck just happened?"

"Well, it seems somebody didn't like us all holding hands."

"Bullshit! They were coming for you, and you knew it."

"I didn't know it until we held hands. I felt them in the crowd."

"But why do they want YOU dead?"

"Seriously?"

"Yeah, what in heaven's name …"

I rephrase.

"What in God's name do they want you dead for? You live and you look like a bum."

He is still wheezing.

"Thanks. My reputation lurking around 'this' library and a few others, and touching a few souls has drawn the attention of some of the more radical Christians, maybe Muslims, but I don't think it was the Jews this time."

"Religious people? Religious people want to kill you?"

"That's how it usually happens, at least most of the time through history. You've got to remember that with religion, or should I say with disproving religion, or just not agreeing with a certain way of thinking, has a way to make religious people very upset. I'm too tired tonight to get back into history, but most wars, genocide, ethnic cleansing, crimes against humanity, The Holocaust, mass executions, race exterminations or just good old-fashion annihilation are pretty much motivated by religion or religious beliefs. How can people say they are religious or believe in 'their' god, and then turn around and hurt each other? There is no love there."

"But why kill you?"

"I guess they think I am dangerous to their existence. It is the way it was a couple thousand years ago when I was Jesus or thirty some years ago when I was John Lennon and many more."

"You're dangerous?"

"Yeah, I know. I don't think I look dangerous. I'm just really hungry."

"How can you be so calm and hungry? We were just shot at!"

"You get used to it and start expecting it."

He starts foraging for food to eat in a crumpled fast food bag tossed to the curb from, I assume, a car.

243

"I just didn't want you to get hit. Are you sure you didn't? You're really bloody."

       I look down at the front of my shirt and from my midsection to my shoes I am soaked in blood and there is so much of it, it has yet to dry. As my adrenalin slows, I start feeling my body again. With the chilly air, and the quantity of blood all over me, my pants feel very heavy and are soaked through to my boxers. My shoes make a squeezed-sponge noise when my foot hits the pavement, oozing blood through the eyelets and tongue of the shoe. The front of my shirt is also covered in bone and chunks of flesh from the size of a piece of lint to one I flecked off me the size of a large marble. It had skin and hair on it. I am nauseated.

"Shit."

"What?"

"We can't walk into a restaurant in these clothes."

"Sure we can. There is nothing in this bag besides ketchup. We've got to go."

       With his incisor, he tears open a ketchup packet and begins to suck on it. He doesn't use his hands to do either move.

"I got an idea. Let's go this way."

       God sounds like Bogart with the ketchup pack hanging out of his mouth. We change directions and begin to head right, then down an alley, but still away from the library, so I am happy we are moving away from danger.

"Where are we going now?"

"We'll be quick."

       It didn't take long, three minutes walk. The evil energy has left the air and is replaced by a street-light-free, dark silence. For the first time in my life I felt more comfortable in the tar-black shroud of a poorly lit alley than a public place. Two days ago I wouldn't have walked down this alley with armed escorts. I couldn't help feeling criminally cool for some reason. God, this journey has evoked emotions I never thought I had.

"Quiet."

      I stand still. God presses his ear to a back door of a building. There are no signs on the walls, but it really is in need of a paint job. Ten or so plastic garbage bags of who knows what, probably garbage, are stacked up on both sides of the door. God rocks back from the door; I figure he was going to kick it open. Instead, he looks to the left and then to the right, turns the handle slowly, perhaps expecting an alarm to go off. It doesn't so he twists it, and the door opens inward.

"Come on."

      We walk into the building and God slowly closes the door until it latches shut. My heart rate begins increase. I never broke into a business before. The smell of stale, old clothes, moth ball attic and dried sweat hangs pungent in the air.

"Where are we?"

"The Salvation Army."

"The what?"

"The Salvations Army Thrift Store: It's where people donate stuff they don't want anymore. It's the world's longest running garage sale."

      I wonder if my old furniture is here.

"You broke into a garage sale?"

"Thrift store. It's where I get all my clothes."

"Why were you listening to the door and how did you get it to open?"

245

"Sometimes they let a dog loose in here."

"And the lock?"

"It's cheap, so you can wiggle it open. I sleep in here sometimes in the winter when the weather is bad. Over here."

> The only light in the room is supplied by a metallic, white, tabletop Christmas tree with one of those revolving red, blue, and yellow lights, at the base of the tree, making the tree and tonight, everything in the room, including us, turn a different color every ten seconds.

> I peel off my clothing except for my blood soaked boxers. The blood has dried on my skin and it doesn't come off by rubbing at it.

"You are going to need a shower to get that off. Right now let's just get changed and get out of here."

> God takes me to the blue jeans rack, then points to the flannel shirts in the next row over. They all smell worn, stored in a cedar armpit, then hung here to sell for 50 cents. I scowl at God when thinking about having to put on someone else's old clothes. My elitist moment passes when I see my reflection in the window: naked except for blood soaked boxers, socks, hair a tangled mess, two-day beard, and dried blood all over me. I don't even know who I am right now.

"They are in size order. So you should be right about in the middle."

> I find myself trying to look for something I like: thrift shop fashionista jeans and a red flannel shirt with a small checkered, pattern. Not bad. I finish the ensemble with an Army jacket and work-boots one size too big. I see God putting on jeans and a shirt. We gravitate toward each other near the Christmas tree and disco light. We stand an arm's reach apart. We are now dressed the same: flannel shirt, jeans, boots, he kept his gym shoe and tongue less boot, and an army jacket; God chuckles.

"What's so funny?"

"You're changing color right in front of my eyes."

"What?"

The light rotates to yellow.

"See? Now you're Asian."

I glace at my reflection in a cracked, Budweiser bar mirror hung on the wall with 'no-one-will-buy-these' old, sun-faded hotel room art prints. I didn't look Asian. I look mustard yellow. The color wheel rotates again. I am now reflecting red.

"What tribe are you? Cherokee?"

The color wheel rotates to bright, rich blue.

"Avatar!"

I begin to laugh.

"Who? I'm, not familiar with that species."

"You know James Cameron?

"Is he their leader?"

"Forget it."

God starts heading for the back door.

"Hold on."

I whisper loudly.

"What?"

"We have to pay for the clothes."

Talk to God

"I don't have any money. They know me here."

"They don't know me."

> I grab my wallet in my back left cheek pocket and notice my new jeans have some 1980s designer pattern with sequins sewn in to the back pocket. Fuck! Great. I pull out a $20 bill. It, too, has blood on one of the edges. I place it in a tip jar on the counter that has three pennies and a paper clip in it. The color wheel revolves again changing my skin color and clothes. God watches me change from color to color.

"Do you feel any different when you are yellow than when you are red? Do you feel dumber? Do you feel less of a human? Do you feel richer? How about poorer? Do you feel less or more entitled? Do you?"

"No."

"How about when you are blue? Does that make you less human since you don't fit into to any color or ethnicity on earth?"

"What?"

> Then it dawns on me: God's schooling me on race.

"I get it. Good point. No, I feel the same on the inside regardless of my color."

"Remember that."

> We walk out the door and back into the alley. God latches the door closed, and we head toward an open restaurant.

33

*You don't know how hungry you are until stale rolls
at Denny's start looking really good to you.*

"Do you want to take a cab? I have money."

*"I know a place about ten minutes walking distance from here. We can talk a little bit
more. We don't have much more time together."*

> I give up guessing what he means by these cryptic
statements like that and now just assume he knows what's going
on and when it is going to happen.

"What else are you curious about?"

"Can I get your opinion on some things in the world today?"

"Sure. I don't think my opinion means too much to anyone, but go for it."

"You are really hard on religion. Is there anyone doing it right out there?"

*"You can have religions, but the only useful ones are based on love. As I said earlier, I
think religions should take their place promoting, protecting, and insuring the clarity of
the message of love. The message just got lost. There are many churches within certain
religions that are getting it right. I love those. They don't get stuck on the ceremony of
hard-line religious beliefs, but have instead found the love I speak of and share it with
their congregation."*

249

"Be specific: Where should I go to find my God's approved places of worship?"

"I got two favorites, well actually one now that the other has already evolved."

"Which ones?"

"Santa Monica, California, Saint Monica's Catholic Church, 9:30 mass with Monsignor Lloyd Turgenson. The guy truly gets it all. He is just stuck being a Catholic priest, but he supports all man-kind and struggles to navigate the shackles of the Catholic Church. But man, the mass is a celebration in song and love. The place is rocking. They sing the 'Our Father' all holding hands, and the place is energized like it was in front of the library before it turned on us. And the power comes from him and everyone in there."

"Who was the other guy?"

"Father Tom Cunningham, Detroit, Michigan. Heck, I once thought he was God! Besides the church you got to check out how this man helped millions, and I mean millions of people through something he did outside the church called; 'Focus Hope.' It was an idea that he came up with to help people in need of food, shelter, education and jobs and the concept was based on 'never judge,' just help and love each other. He evolved to the next level a few years ago. You want talk about a guy that is flying around the universe. He has the love of millions within him. He could build a universe someday. He and Turgenson, both priests reaching outside the boundaries of the church but both staying faithful to be church's biblical principles. I give them both credit for trying. My moles on the inside! They are or were so powerful the religions should have been taking their cues from them regarding love. They know how to love and share love."

God laughs while mumbling again; "moles on the inside."

"Anyone else you dig on earth?"

"Blood, Water Mission."

"What?"

"Check out a Christian band called Jars of Clay. They are four young men who have a mission to drill fresh-water wells throughout Africa to help people living without potable water. They use their platform as musical entertainers to promote the mission. Song brings people together, and the work they do is truly exceptional. These are just a few faves. There are hundreds of others doing great things out there."

"What do you not like?"

"Motherless children: Every kid needs a mom even if it is not their birth mom. The rules of life transcend through love. When a child is motherless he loses his way and often becomes hateful. A kid needs a mom."

"Anything else jump at you that really upsets you?"

"Lost true love."

> Silence. Oh shit, another gut-wrenching emotional lesson from God regarding my dead wife.

"Really? Not again? I'm really too tired and pretty frazzled for a lesson on lost love."

"No, we're cool. You've found love again. You are healing."

> God stops walking. We are standing in front of a restaurant that stays open late.

"Ready, I'm starved."

> Decent neighborhood: a few vagrants hiding in the shadows, but no gun-shots, screaming babies, barking dogs, or screeching tires.

"Hold on! Have you ever been in here before?"

"No, looked too fancy for me. I usually have a couple dollars from taking empties back but this place looks like it will cost a lot of money."

> We walk into the Denny's with our new "old" clothes not looking quite as homeless as we did a half hour before, a little

251

more like Seattle grunge, garage band. I'm much more comfortable knowing this may be a quiet meal with God with a little more time to pick his brain. We sit at a counter. It runs down the long side of the restaurant, separating the kitchen from the dining booths and tables.

"You never sit in a booth?"

"I like the counter best. The service is quicker."

And it was quick; as soon as our butts hit the stools we were greeted by a pipe cleaner of a woman: tall, bony, hip bones protruding from her forward slumping, bad posture, who delivers us water and two menus in a split second. God is impressed with the water given with no request.

"See? Fancy!"

He gulps down the water and almost as quickly as his glass hits the Formica counter-top, it is filled again with a pitcher as the woman passes by, never spilling a drop, nor hardly slowing her pace.

"I told you: fancy."

I think the restaurant was pretty busy for a late Saturday night. Maybe it was the movie crowd, but there must have been 35 people here. The specials are written on a chalk-board at the entrance that I could read from my stool. Fish and chips: $7.75; hamburger and fries: $6.50; some skillet thing that sounds too complicated, and the soup of the day was beef barley. Our waitress circles back to us, draws out her pad and pen, and wheezes in a smoker's, sand-papery inhale to ask us for our order when God starts in.

"Hamburger, two orders of fries, and more water, please."

She looks a bit surprised, but not startled with his curt order. It was a Denny's not the Ritz; she has had odder characters in here before. I try to show some manners for the both of us.

"Thanks so much; ma'am. I would like to have the fish and chips please, ma'am."

She writes down our order, smiles, and leaves.

"Call me Mary honey, ma'am makes me feel old."

Great, he has no manners, and I sound like Rain-man. What a couple! Her next pass brings us a cheap, plastic, red-wicker basket with a paper napkin covering three rolls. Now these rolls must have been on yesterday's bread truck: They were hard to the touch and they had that 'too-much-cheap flour' covering the bottoms of them; two pumpernickel (who eats pumpernickel?), and one of wheat, with dried onion flecks on the top that reminded me of ants. It crosses my mind just how many times these rolls have been brought out, not eaten, and then taken back, nuked warm, and put in another basket to be served. They seem stale enough to be on their fifth cycle. God notices the buns but with more enthusiasm and less concern for their present state.

"Did you order those?"

"No, it probably comes with the meal."

"Told you! Fancy!"

You don't know how hungry you are until stale rolls at Denny's start looking really good to you. I decide to give the whole wheat with the onion flecks that remind me of ants a try. My reach is interrupted by God's dirty hand grabbing the basket and putting it in front of him.

"I know you said you were hungry but I thought I could have that one roll there."

"Listen, you got fish coming and I got a hamburger and fries coming. What do you say we see if someone else who is hungry may need it more than we do?"

Figures. God pulls back the napkin and starts ripping the buns with his bare hands into four smaller pieces making what looks like twelve dried chunks of bread. Birds would probably find it less appetizing. God then stands up, oh shit, and takes the basket with him. He walks around, throughout the restaurant, systematically looking at every person there. He finds that most people have their food in front of them and do not require the bread since most have the same basket of dried-out rolls on their table too.

He finally arrives at a table with four young, high-school girls; juniors, maybe seniors - it's been too long. They are all sipping water or soda and texting on their phones, but probably not there to eat. I cannot hear what God is saying to them over the din of the crowd, but I see him gesturing, inviting them to eat a piece of the bread. They giggle and decline, and it now dawns on him that everyone in the restaurant has food at their table or the same crappy basket of rolls. Never detoured, he scans his surroundings and through the large plate glass windows, he sees a group of older men looking very homeless, outside the restaurant, with their shopping carts full of their live's and two with roller suit-cases stocked with all their worldly possessions. He quickly exits the restaurant with the basket and takes the bread over to them.

They are positively excited and happy to receive the bread. He waits until they have taken every last piece, then after a few handshakes and a few pats on the back, he moves swiftly back into the restaurant. It goes without saying that God's bread stunt has now caught the attention of some of the patrons in the restaurant. He quickly rushes back in and right up to me.

"Give me your water."

"What?"

"May I have your water, please?"

He doesn't really wait for my approval and takes my glass and his and asks Mary if she could fill them up. She doesn't notice his intent. But in an instant he is heading back outside with water for the men. As he passes one of the tables, a mother and her three children are sitting in a booth, kids all under the ages of ten and eating chicken fingers and fries. The woman stops him by holding out her basket of stale buns. She motions with the basket: take it. He stops to thank her and presses the basket under his left elbow and against his body so he can carry the glasses without spilling. More people in the restaurant are beginning to watch God in action.

When he gets back out to the four men, he gives them the water and kneels down on the pavement to divide the three rolls that were donated to his cause by the woman. Again, the homeless men are buzzing with excitement. I can see through the window the talk between God and the four men has turned joyful with smiles, laughter, and hugs. Five more homeless people see food being distributed and join the group and then three more. God kneels and begins to divide the bread into pieces, which he again distributes to the now larger crowd of homeless people, but he is short on bread for the 12 and apologizes. He brings the empty basket and the two empty plastic glasses back into the restaurant. He is vexed knowing he is short. His eyes scan the restaurant looking for more bread.

Mary delivers our food. Bingo! I see his eyes light up. The fish and chips actually look really good: piping hot with the smell of cold slaw in one of those little paper cups, the tartar sauce in a smaller one, lemon wedge, French fries all melded into this amazing aroma by the fresh from the fryer, golden brown, deep fried fish. Boy, it smells so good my mouth actually waters. God's hamburger and fries look succulent, as if snatched right from the menu photo. Out of the corner of my eye I notice the twelve men are still there, and it dawns on me that this is probably not going to end quickly. I hurriedly take a bite of my cod and shove a wad of fries into my mouth, never getting a taste of the creamy cold slaw before God returns.

"May I have your …?"

I don't even hesitate lifting my dinner toward him. He grabs my plate, then his, stacking the fries on top of his burger, carrying it in his left, mine in his right, then races for the door with that dumb little gimpy walk; gym shoe, boot, gym shoe, boot, with the enthusiasm of a waiter bustling out from the kitchen of a white linen restaurant. When he arrives back to the group he stops them from pushing to get to the food, and motions for some decorum. Honor and manners among thieves and the homeless, I guess.

They stand quietly now bursting with anticipation as God divides the second course into bite-sized pieces. He gives every one of them a fair portion of our dinner, never once sneaking a fry for himself. He quickly wheels and starts back into the restaurant. Now what? I figure he would now want my new, old clothes or something. Mary is waiting for him with a tray of glasses filled to the brim with icy cold water and a smile from ear to ear. He immediately spins back around and delivers the water as all 12 now sit quietly against a wall outside the restaurant in the parking lot. The parking lot lights give everyone in the restaurant a clear view of God in action and put an odd glow on the twelve men sitting against the wall. Mary watches with a new-found joy and enthusiasm. She can feel something special was going on. She stops and looks at me.

"You're with him. Who is he?"

"You really want to know?

"Yeah."

"Before I tell you, take a few minutes and see if you can figure it out."

34

He looks at me and sees optimism through my hollowed out,
reddened eyes, barely attached anymore to
what's left of my broken heart.

I really get her curiosity churning. I didn't want to play games, but shit, when you say it out loud it really sounds like you are nuts. I do feel like the posse of a rock star. I sit on my stool now rotated, so my back is leaning on the empty counter, to keep an eye on him, making sure no one fucks with him. I glance around the restaurant and everyone's eyes are fixed on God. As the homeless men outside against the wall eat, God mesmerizes them with his wrap. I know what's coming. God extends his hands, and I could see him motioning to have everyone hold hands in a chain making a human circle. Reluctant, and concerned about detaching from all of their worldly possessions, God finally coaxes them into clasping hands, motioning them to put their important belongings right at their feet. As soon as all hands are clasped, he slams his whammy on them.

I, along with all the patrons in the restaurant watch as joy, tears of happiness, warm memories begin to flow, reminding them of lost loves, fallen friends, better days, and lost family - feelings that haven't crossed their minds or lifeless souls in decades. Their emotions go from depression at their lot in life to total bliss. Four of the 12 men drop straight to their knees on the pavement. Three others begin crying uncontrollably. I am sure these will be moments that will change their lives, probably for the better. Maybe it was contact with an evolved friend or family member, maybe an abandoned wife forgiving him, or a mental message from a son or daughter that it became too hard for them to see their father destroy himself with drugs or alcohol but want him back. Whatever their experience was it moved them all in all separate ways. It was eerie. But it was so God.

After about five minutes of personal reflection, the attention turns back to the group as a whole as God addresses them aloud. As he speaks, the group starts swaying back and forth to the melody of God's message of love. Seeing 12 lost souls become united and truly enjoying something was breath-taking.

Everyone in the restaurant is now out of their chairs and at the windows fixated on the impromptu food drive and outdoor revival. Some have been drawn outside to get a closer look. His tracking beam is truly powerful. The group's hands, still clasped, sway as God continues to speak to them about his love, not to be selfish, and start giving back to mankind because this is the way to a loving future after they evolve. And I got to tell you, they believe and they are riveted.

A man, in the restaurant, four stools down, small in stature, old, and alone, rises from his seat, and takes his hot, freshly delivered turkey sandwich, smothered in gravy, out to the group and hands it to God, who thanks the man then immediately begins splitting up the food up into equal portions again while kneeling. God places the hands of the people he was holding on top of his head so he doesn't break the chain. The man that donated the turkey sandwich joins the circle, and is swallowed into the ocean of the power of the universe: love. He can't stop smiling. It is contagious. He begins to cry, clearly tears of joy. I am sure he has just said hello to his dead wife or a loved one.

One after another, nine people in the restaurant take their entire plate of food out to the twelve. They are swamped with more food than they know what to do with. It was truly a bounty for all; so much so that some of the food brought out was also given to the donor, in portions. People helping and loving people, is cool. In today's society, I can't believe what I am seeing. This guy's got mad ass fucking skills.

The manager of the restaurant and two bus-boys bring out three large trays of white cake frosted with those bright red cherries neatly placed in the middle of each piece cut into single portions, for everyone to enjoy. This draws more people, people that aren't homeless. God waves passers-by to join the event and feast on the bounty. The restaurant manager has the bus-boys make sure that all the glasses were refilled to the top with their choice of water or iced tea. He is rushing to get everyone whatever they need not expecting any payment.

God motions to the bus-boys to get the manager to join the chain. The manager comes over timidly and stands next to God. An odd energy jolt freezes the group holding hands. They stop enjoying their personal moments and focus their attention on God and the manager. He looks frightened but extends his hands, inviting himself into the chain at the closest point of the energy source. God opens his clasped hand and allows the manager into the chain. But before he does, God stares deep into the manager's eyes and taps his own chest by his heart with his fist and signifying to 'be strong'. This is different. I never saw God do that.

When the circle was reconnected the restaurant manager begins to literally convulse and is falling chin-first toward the pavement. The only thing stopping him from planting his face in the asphalt was God and the person next to the manager holding his hands and slowing his fall. His eyes roll back. He looks in real trouble. The entire crowd watching and participating lurches forward and gasps. Something is very strange about the managers his reaction.

I stop one of the bus-boys who have been running in and out with food and drinks.

"Hey! Hey, Amigo!"

The bus-boy comes over looking distressed wanting to get back to attend to his manager.

"Did anything bad every happen to your boss?"

It fucking freezes him. In broken English with a heavy Spanish accent, he swallows hard.

"What do jew mean?"

"Someone he knows die or something?"

His chin drops to his chest.

"Ow, did jew know?"

"Know what?"

"Ez family of seven keeds and his wife were killed in a car accident and e' was driving, jus' two years ago. He was de only one to leave."

"Fuck!"

The bus-boy crosses himself, and scurries away, pointing to the wall behind the counter. Above the register are a crucifix and a family portrait of the manager, his wife, and seven children. He had triplets that looked about four years old. They were in their Sunday best. Fuck, and I am bumming? Shame on me! Maybe this is why we came? I feel so ashamed to be so shitty and whining all weekend. And I thought I had demons. How does this man get up in the morning?

There are two police officers in the restaurant sitting in the back, actually trying to stay out of the action but when they hear the shrills as the manager just about hit the pavement, they decide they need to go and find out what the heck was going on. I try to intercept the officers quickly, because I know the manager will be better and will get through this and will begin to heal.

"Officers?"

No attention to my call.

"OFFICERS!"

Now loud. They stop. I approach them.

"That man will be fine. He had a horrible ordeal a few years back. He lost his entire family and I promise you that man out there-"

I point to God. They both look at God - in all his homelessness - holding the manager.

"-what he has done to help people who have lost someone is amazing."

Of course, they look at me like I am full of shit. Then the shorter of the two huge officers glances at his partner.

OFFICER 1: "*Mitch you lost your wife last year.*"

OFFICER 2: "*So what?*"

He doesn't like that his partner sharing personal information.

"I lost my wife a few months ago. I can't tell you the guy saved me. You should go out there."

OFFICER 2: "*Go for it. What do you have to lose?*"

OFFICER 1: "*Fuck it.*"

"Seriously, go."

He looks at me and sees optimism through my hallowed out, reddened eyes, barely attached anymore to what's left of my broken heart. He knows the look of despair from what he sees every morning in the mirror. He knows that look of pain. He knows the look you have after you've cried all night and are expected to continue to work and live alone. He sees right into my heart. Two empty, blackened, souls make for comfortable bedfellows. He knows. He sees it in my eyes. We've walked the same path. He nods his head and heads out. I stop his partner.

"Let him go alone. He'll need the space."

Back outside God attends to the manager. He lets his hands free, breaking the human love chain. The group quickly circles around the man who is convulsing on the ground. God waves the cop over to help lift the man up. As I watch I get the distinct feeling that this has been all choreographed by God well before any of it happens.

The manager looks like he could be having a heart attack. God instructs the police officer to lift the man up so he is eye level with God. As the officer holds him under his arms from behind, still in great duress, God pulls the manager's eye-lids back so he can see God piercing stare. The manager is in and out of consciousness. God is speaking to him in Spanish, but he doesn't look good. Fuck! Don't die! Don't die with the cops there! God's facial expression is calm, confident, and happy. God looks up at the cop.

OFFICER 1: "_Help him. He has stopped breathing._"

"_You can help him. You have the strength and the love still in your heart. You help him._"

OFFICER 1: "_No I don't . My life ended last year. I have nothing left to give._"

"_No it didn't. It just began with Marilyn and will someday for you, too._"

OFFICER 1: "_How do you know my wife's…._"

The officer's sentence goes unfinished as God stares into his sullen eyes, and the cop knows now why he knows.

OFFICER 1: "_What should I do? The defibrillator is back in the squad!_"

"_You have the love in your heart to save him. Feel it. Use it. Ask Marilyn to help you. We are all here to help you, to help each other._"

The police officer hikes the man up from under the arm pits, higher into his grasp so their heads are now side by side. The officer's mouth is pressed to the manager's ear;

OFFICER 1*: "Baby, I know I talk to you every day about bad things and sad things in my life, in my mind, but honey forget about that now, this is really important. If you can hear me, this man really needs our help now."*

"She is with us now."

God takes a step toward them and places his hands, one on the officer's forehead and the other on the manager's forehead. I know this trick. As quick as his hand touches their heads a jolt of energy rushes through both their bodies. They lurch as a massive cleansing breath fills their lungs at the same time. The group of people holding hands now circle around the men and place their hands on their bodies, anywhere there was an open area. God tells them both to breathe and within three large breaths, both men begin to find physical, and for the first time in a long time, mental solace, mental peace. The manger slumps into the police officers embrace. The police officer begins to cry through a wide smile, nodding his head to God in appreciation. The two broken men have seen the ones they loved, and love, and now they know they are okay lying in the hands of God. Mother Fuckin' A!

The people with their hands on the men step back and begin to clap. Of course there is a world of cosmic sweat all over everyone but the moment of grave concern turns to total bliss. Within five minutes, the manager is happy as hell. With a birthday smile on his face the manager bows in front of God and begins kissing his hands. The cop waits his turn to pay homage to God. God makes them both stand up and asks them to join the reforming circle that has doubled in number of participants. Cheers go up for the manager and the cop. One of the bus-boys comes over and hugs the manager tightly and won't let go. The celebration is now really cooking.

A crowd of people, some passing by, some going into the restaurant to eat, had stopped to watch the feast and celebration. The police officer's partner walks up to the reformed, now much larger circle of human love, and invites himself, in between a homeless man on one side of him, and a young man with gang tattoos on the other, to allow him into the chain.

Shit! As soon as he linked with the group you could see the love wash over him, and he began uncontrollably crying, loud, big, wailing, lumpy tears, pouring down his face. I can't imagine the weight and suffering police officers carry in their hearts. The world needs to stop the pain someday. The collateral damage with the people who care is immense. You could see the shine from his tears on his cheeks glisten from the parking lot lights. He begins to shake, then wobble, then falls to his knees as he howls uncontrollably. A subset of people rush to put their hands on the officer.

More people exit the restaurant with food and money for the 12 and anyone else in need. The circle has turned into a large mass of people. It was a crowd of love. One woman gave a man her coat, another a sweat shirt. The woman with her three kids assists the bus-boys in passing out more white cake. The four teen girls come out, more curious than anything, and joined the circle, and started singing "All You Need Is Love." I didn't think they even knew the song much less the words. As their tiny alto voices are noticed, the group picks up the melody, and everyone, and I mean everyone, begins to sing.

Love, Love, Love.
Love, Love, Love.
Love, Love, Love.

There's nothing you can do that can't be done.
Nothing you can sing that can't be sung.
Nothing you can say, but you can learn how to play the game.
It's easy.

All you need is love.
All you need is love.
All you need is love, love.

Love is all you need.

Over and over they sang. And the fact that the girls chose a Beatles song, God's song, and not Taylor Swift in the middle of all this - this what? - this non-religious, religious experience, is well beyond me but probably exactly what God wants. The people not in circle who were watching began to clap and sing as well. The number of people in the parking lot has swelled to well over 200. People saw what was happening and began joining the spectacle.

After about three verses and a lot of "love, love, love," repeated over and over, God walks to the middle of the circle and raises his hands over his head. He then bends at the waist, a big old opera style bow, and the group followed, kind of like a hand holding wave at a sporting event. God releases his grasp and the chain slowly breaks apart and the energy cycles down. Everyone, and again, I mean every "fucking" one, is euphoric and begins to hug and kiss and love everyone else - total strangers no longer. Even the cop in huge pain has found peace, his arms wrapped around the manager and his partner, now all crying with joy. No one wants to leave. These are all good friends now.

Unpretentiously God smiles and nods to anyone who approaches, handshakes and hugs abound all around him. People walk up to him and drop to their knees reaching for his hands. He would rest his hand on their foreheads and bless them? I guess that is what you would call he was doing. I know he is turning on their love light, so I guess blessing them is a fine way to describe it. He'd probably be pissed at me for calling it that since he is not religious. It's fucking funny: God not being religious.

35

Who stands outside the abortion clinic when those
children come out - broken, sad, lost, full of inconsolable guilt?
Who? Who hugs them? Who loves them? I DO!

For the next half hour about 25 to 30 people, wait to
kneel in front of him, pope-like. When the last one was finished,
he says his goodbyes and then heads back into the restaurant
where he is met by applause. I mean a standing, fucking ovation.
Rock n' roll Jesus! My God! When we get back to our stools my
newly prepared fish and chips await and for God there is a
hamburger, and two bountiful orders of fries. He takes a one bite
and starts jamming the remainder of the food into his pockets.

"Stop!"

He is strangely startled by my firmness.

"Mary!"

I call our spindly server and God's aqua wingman from
the waitress station.

"Could you put my good friend's food in a take home container please?"

266

She smiles and agrees to do so without hesitation. Within a half minute she is back with a clam shell-shaped Styrofoam container with his food inside, plastic fork, knife and spoon, salt, pepper, and napkins all dressed nicely in a large take-home bag. My food is the same way. She places it in front of him on the counter and leans over, holds his unwashed cheeks with both of her hands, and kisses him smack on the lips. She then slides her hands down to his on the counter top and kisses them as you might when meeting royalty. Tears of joy stream down her boney, wrinkled cheeks. I knew she would figure out who he was.

We stand to pay our check and are met at the register by three men, one in his early twenties in a suit and tie, the other two in their forties in casual dress, all wanting to take care of our tab. The manager has beaten them all to the punch and waves them all away after giving God a big bear hug. The manager has the photo of his family that was on the wall now under his arm. He looks at God, bows, and thanks him again, then kisses the photo and holds it to his heart. God returns the warm wishes, walks out the door, looks to the left and then to the right, spies a homeless woman, walking, and hands over the entire take-home bag with our dinner. Shit.

"I thought you were hungry?"

"They were all hungrier."

We begin walking down the street.

"Where are we going?"

"Where do you want to go?"

I think about it for a long moment.

"I think I am ready to go home"

God stops for a minute and draws a long, hard stare, deep into my eyes. He doesn't say a word for what seems like five minutes.

267

Talk to God

"What?"

"I think you are, too."

God smiles at me, but this time the smile was a father's smile, full of subtle satisfaction, knowing he is proud of me and happy that I am healing. He was right.

"How far are we from your apartment?"

"It is probably around five or six miles."

"That won't take too long. We can talk some more if you want."

I don't really know what to ask anymore. So much has happened. I walked more today and yesterday than I have walked in a lifetime. And shit, my fish was also in that doggy bag. God seems at ease though, chipper even, and we have become comfortable with each other.

"I got a question for you. Have you ever watched a sporting event and see guys pray to you after they hit a big home-run, or score a winning touchdown?"

"You already know I don't judge; it's all free will. What they should do at large gatherings, like sporting events, is get the crowd warmed up, and excited, and jointly root for their player or team. I've seen that happen. The crowd, the support and love, can make a person be more successful in a sporting event just like we do when we hold hands or hug. Love is a powerful thing. Praying to me after hitting a home slam is a waste of time."

Home slam...Mr. Baseball.

"Okay, forget that for a minute. Presently The Russians and The Americans, and even some smaller countries, have enough nuclear weapons to blow all humans off the face of the earth and send us into a nuclear winter..."

"I probably won't show up as often if that occurs."

268

"What happens to the planet?"

"Well besides screwing it up for a couple million years, not much more. The idiots who thought more of themselves than for other people will become the next archeological find, and you will start all over again. A few millions of years to you are a blink of an eye to the big universe and the big picture."

"What happens to all the people?"

"As you now know, they all evolve at all levels. The only thing different about this is that there will be so many in such a short period of time, the cosmic tumblers will probably be on overload. No civilization has yet ever destroyed itself in the universe, so I can't really give you an accurate reference. Do your best not to screw it up and be the first."

"What do you, God, love most about the earth?

"Ah, these are too easy. I love young children the best, before they are pressed into your society's systematic formation of poor behavior, bad manners, out-of-focus education, and just general rudeness. They live with the simple ease of knowing their mom, and hopefully their dad, love them. They have a warm and safe place to live and have food to eat. Before they go to school they have not been scarred by a performance based, pressure-cooker society trapped in fear and self-confidence issues. Yuck! Young children are the beacon of hope for everyone. We all should take a lesson or two from a four year old."

"If you wanted to share one piece of information with the world that is not about love, what would it be?"

"Forgiveness. When pain, which usually evolves into hatred, exists between two people, it does not allow for love to grow. You cannot grow love when you are harboring hatred for someone or something. In fact, if an individual darkens his heart with hate, it will eventually eat him alive from the soul outward, until he is dead and doesn't remember what love is. Hate is a powerful adversary. These people who don't forgive usually have a lonely existence after their evolution. So world…"

God raises his arms in the air and screams.

"Love and Forgive!"

"Can you forgive abortion?"

269

"Sure. That one is easy. Free will has its good things and its bad things. I don't personally dig any destruction of human life. Now, that being said, the rules of the universe, free will and the accumulation of love, your energy, also apply to people contemplating having an abortion."

"What are you trying to say?"

"If there is immense pain and fear in someone's heart who is contemplating having an abortion, their heart will search for love, and usually in your society today they will find only great sorrow. When the pity and sorrow grow in one's heart, it destroys love and the person is scarred with bitterness and loses some of their ability to love unconditionally ever again. Plus the mind will eat their heart out with guilt. It is sad when a heart gets hurt so bad it may never recover."

God shoots me a look.

"We need to surround these people with love, and I don't mean those freaky ass-bags hanging around abortion clinics with baby strollers and photos of dead fetuses yelling at children when they are walking in. You want to talk about people devoid of love, with hate in their hearts? Talk to those freaks. They need more love than those kids going into the abortion clinic. They are usually there because of guilt themselves.

"Not to digress, but the pain of an abortion is not a public pain, it is internal strife that is destructive. The fallout from an abortion is the psychological destruction it does to the woman as well as the unborn child. There are no winners in this."

"Still they are taking a life when they enter one of those clinics."

"Please do not get high and mighty with Mr. High and Mighty regarding abortion. I don't. Similarly, I also do not judge soldiers who kill another soldier or a civilian. Do I judge dictators who commit genocide? No. Do I judge a drunken parent who beats their child to death? No. Abortion is no different. It is a loss of life from another's hand. As bad as you or others may think that is, I can't decide to judge a certain thing that society has trouble with at the present time, or any of the other things you all do to destroy yourselves. Some of the shit you do to each other is unimaginable."

"But don't you think it's a soldier's patriotic duty to fight and possibly kill to protect our country, our way of life?"

270

"I assume you're talking about today and your way of life here in America. Do you hear yourself? How do you destroy life to protect your way of life? It is no one's duty to kill anyone regardless of today's politics. This "duty" that you speak of for your country, changes every century. You believe you are right to take a life in the name of patriotism. Did Mohammad and the Muslims believe that in 600 C.E.? How about Genghis Khan at the start of the 12th century? How about something closer to today? Did Mao Ze-Dong in China in 1958, feel it was his patriotic duty to kill 75 million people? How about Stalin in the 1930s? Do you think it was his duty to kill 23 million, Hitler 12 million, Tojo in Japan in the 1940s, 5 million, Brezhnev almost a million in Afghanistan; was that in the name of the Motherland? And today do you believe it is your patriotic duty to kill over one million Iraqi people, soldiers and civilians in the name of what, patriotism, liberty, or just oil?"

I am fucked on this topic.

"Causes, rulers, and governments change all the time. What doesn't change is a human's responsibility to love, share love and stand up against killing of another human-life. Knowing what you know now of what happens when you evolve, could you ever raise a hand, much less your voice to anyone now that you are aware that it will impact your future? This will all change in a number of centuries when you all develop and start to get it."

"Remember, with love comes respect, pride, and dignity. When a teenage girl gets pregnant, the primary reason why she considers an abortion is because she is not embraced in love by the guy, her family, and friends. She becomes alienated, an outcast, frightened, and is immersed in stress, pain, and fear - sometimes to the brink of suicide. This person needs us all the most right then, and what do you do?"

I shake my head not actually knowing what is coming.

"You treat her like a leper at the time she is the most full of life. If there is love around her, support from all - like it will be someday - abortion will become a thing of the past, not because of birth control or some of those fucking loons out in front of abortion clinics, but because of the love that surrounds the woman and everyone one of us. She will become keenly aware of the love around her and feel confident in keeping the baby or giving it to a family who is less fortunate because of the love and support of her friends and family. You know what less fortunate means?"

"I KNOW! We couldn't have children because of me. Fuck you! Thanks!"

271

"Relax. There is room and a home for every baby. There is room in our hearts for woman that go through an abortion. Who stands outside the abortion clinic when those children come out; broken, sad, lost, full of inconsolable guilt? Who? Who hugs them? Who loves them? I DO! And you should too! That's when they need it the most. You all must unconditionally love everyone else without prejudice or malice, regardless of the whys and what for's. Guide and love lost souls, then support them regardless of their decision. Same with soldiers in the name of patriotism: they come home broken and who loves them? Where can they find love with the black demons swirling around in their heads and hearts? Do you know what American soldiers in Iraq found most horrifying?"

"No, what?"

"That the difference between them and an Iraqi is nothing. The Iraqis live in homes with their families, and ninety five percent of them want to live in peace. They want to enjoy their lives and love their families."

The level of God's intensity on this subject has made the walk go quickly. We are a few blocks from my apartment. What a two-day odyssey. I make an attempt to get him off the subject.

36

We arrive at my apartment: a cheap, stucco, 14 unit
Dumpster with no common amenities, just 14 doors,
opening to 14 sad stories - eight hundred square feet of loneliness.

"How long do you want to stay with me?"

"Probably until tomorrow."

"No! Hold the fuck on. I'm just starting to get it. Where are you going? I won't be able to take you leaving me; not now. Please!"

"Let me think about it, but let's not ruin tonight. We still have plenty of time to talk more."

> We arrive at my apartment; a cheap, stucco, 14 unit Dumpster with no common amenities, just 14 doors, opening to 14 sad stories - 800 square feet of loneliness with walls that talk. God follows me through the tiny corridors typical of a cheap, I-don't-give-a-shit-where-I-live places. He is right behind me as I start fumbling for my keys. I unlock the door and start to swing it open. But before it opens half-way, God stops me and turns me around to face him, my back to the apartment door.

"This place is no longer you. When you left Friday, this apartment, like your heart, like your soul, was hollow, empty, with little love and plenty of hate. You have changed. Do not be startled."

        It seems hyperbolic to say that. I turn back half not really caring what he said, and walk through the door. God places his hand on my left shoulder but no whammy or electricity. He knows what is on the other side; I am not so sure anymore. He is letting me ride this out, bench testing my heart and soul. I step through the small entry door. The air is thick, warm, and stale. The aroma of rotten leftovers wafts through the apartment. Thursday night's takeout, and now the Saturday science project, sit on the TV tray. Shit.

"See? This place harbored a broken, loveless man. He no longer exists. You are a loving man."

"I'm a loving man? I am a loving man."

        I am a different man and now I feel like a victim walking through his own crime scene. The black, bilious rush of pain begins to circle me. God tightly squeezes my shoulder muscle and collar-bone but again, no big God trick.

"Think of her."

"No!"

"Think of her now, evolved. Think of her happy. Think of you happy. Think of love."

        My knees wobble.

"I can't! The hate is coming back. It is suffocating me."

        The back of my neck begins to burn. There are no reminders of her, just the hate in the room and shitty chair, the taped box, the pathetic TV table and flat screen leaning against the fucking wall - AND NO HER! The stink of my painful reality returns to me. The hate I made, I feel, I am conjuring now, is palpable. This is solitary. This is my living tomb. I am buried alive. Fuck! This is my living death.

"Love! Come on! Love God Dammit!"

       I close my eyes. I want to go back outside. I want to go back to the streets, to the people, the library, the restaurant. Fuck, I want to go anywhere but here!

"No! This is real! This is your life! This is now. You have to let the hate go! You have to let the love back in."

"I can't! I miss her so!"

"You can! She is around you ....now!"

       I fall to my knees and wail, crying and sobbing! In the depths of my darkest recesses of my mind: hate and pain, hate and pain, hate and pain, fucking hate and pain. FUCK! FUCK! FUCK! What's that? I get real still. I smell, I smell, I smell what? What is that? What the fuck is that? Goddamn! it's, it's, it's, oh shit! It's our Sunday morning. I hear her voice. I focus - hard.

"Stay with it."

       Am I seeing her? Am I hearing her? Screaming!

"Is this you, God?"

"No, it's you, all you. Open up."

       My breath is shallow. I'm sweating. My heart is racing. I want to die so I can be with her. How is my hair?

" Focus. Let her in. She is there. Focus NOW! This is all you!"

       Every muscle in my body trembles, convulsing out of control. I am mush again. The room swirls and tilts. I struggle to stay conscious and focused on her soul. I think I am wide open spiritually and emotionally. Yes? Her soul rushes into mine. Bam!

Oh sweet! You are back! Sweet love. Oh, the beauty and freshness of her soul harbors no pain. Within two deep breaths my hate has been refracted into a million lost and never to be found pieces. I am feeling, no, I am love, true love. I am her, and she me. I hold my breath, afraid to lose focus. No… I got it - and it is wonderful.

I fall to the floor from my knees into fetal comfort. Her image is real. We are sitting in our robes at home, Sunday morning, playing footsie under the table, sipping espresso and thumbing through the color coupon section. She raises her head and tousles her hair and looks right into my eyes.

"I have been with you since that night in the hospital when I evolved. You have been in such great pain. I am sorry I couldn't reach to you, but you were unaware. I miss you dearly, and as sad as you are, my pain only came in seeing you hurting. For where I am and where you are going is wonderful. I always had the knowledge that we would be together forever. Your sadness was perpetuated by not knowing. But fear no longer, our souls are one now and forever. Live with that knowledge. Enjoy the rest of your years until you evolve. It will seem like minutes from now. Love, laugh, and share your love with everyone. It will make the rest of our tomorrows much more enriched. I love you."

She leans over the kitchen table and softly kisses me on the lips. I reach and hold cheeks ever so lightly. I want to die now. I feel myself puckering my lips as I lie on the floor. I drift off into a deep sleep. Finally, oh finally, bliss.

276

37

God gets to his feet and stretches.
You hear bones cracking, farting.
He then rolls his neck until he gets it to crack.

I am awaken by the warmth of the Sunday morning sun flooding the living room through a window that I never, ever drew the drapes back from. For the first time in a long time I feel well rested. The sun feels good as I awake, but within a few minutes it becomes too hot, and I need to pee. I roll from my belly to my back and what is more noticeable than the ceiling that needs painting, is that my only pain is my bloated bladder. I have no morning gut-twist, no aimless lost feeling, and no heartache. It is nice. Thanks, baby.

I get to my feet, now I really have to pee. I quickly look around for God. He is not in the only chair in the room, nor on the floor; in the bedroom, nor the kitchen. He's gone? I've really got to pee. I swing open the bathroom door and start unzipping my fly when the door pushes back. It is God blocking the path of the door, lying on the ceramic tile floor, curled into the corner between the tub and toilet. He has taken off his shirt. The bruises I inflicted on Friday have now blossomed into grotesque, black and blue flesh marks on each side of his rib cage - visual battle scars of my beating. It is almost too hard to look at. Quietly as I possibly can I unzip my fly and piss in the sink trying not to wake him. No good, his eyes flash open when my piss stream hits the cheap, rusted drain making a pinging noise.

"God?"

I whisper.

"God?"

His eyes open slowly; he sees me and smiles. He, too, seems to be emotionally comfortable with the same easy nature. I think he knew I passed a moment last night and my gut tells me that is why he came; sadly, he will probably be leaving soon.

"Why did you take your shirt off?"

"I have learned that my body feels better when I press my skin against the coolness of ceramic tile. It deadens the pain, like ice, helps it heal and allows me to sleep. When my body warms up the tiles where I lie, I just roll over to colder ones, and it makes my other side feel better. How are you?"

I think for a second. I feel like a dick because I caused the pain he is feeling, but that isn't what he was asking.

"I am really, really good."

"Good! I got to get going."

"Whoa! Let's not rush off right away. At least have some breakfast with me."

God gets to his feet and stretches. You hear bones cracking, farting. He then rolls his neck until he gets it to crack. His face looks like a 40-year old's but his body is that of a twenty-two-year-old man who had the shit kicked out of him. I guess being God keeps you in shape.

"Okay, I am really hungry."

"You said that last night, and you didn't eat at all but fed half the city. If we go somewhere to eat will you eat, just sit and eat?"

He buttons his shirt, looks up, smiles, unzips his fly, removes his penis, begins to urinate in the toilet and nods in agreement. I leave the room so he has some privacy - not like it would have mattered to him.

I walk back into the sun drenched living room, the one chair in the center of the room makes it look like an interrogation room in a cop movie instead of living room: TV table, bent and rusted, and flat screen TV against the wall. How pathetic. What an existence. The carpet - colored melted, chocolate, ice cream brown, stains everywhere. The walls: nails hanging out where pictures hung from the last tenant and were not removed. With the sun-light I can now see the shadows of the dirt outlines where the frames had once been. I decide in a split second that I will move out of here on Monday. I wish I had our old house back. The memories are now warm, loving reminders of my life with my bride, no longer a tomb of living nightmares. I think I will go over there later and see if the house is for sale or the owners I sold it to may be planning a move; so much to do all of a sudden. I am breathing and truly living again. God exits the bathroom.

"Ready?"

"You bet, I'm starving."

"Seriously?"

"Seriously."

I thought of changing my clothes, but I didn't want God to feel awkward or out of place, so I am going with the flannel and jeans, the uniform of the creator of the universe. We bounce out of the apartment and walk quickly to the parking lot, talking about anything that isn't important; and that's good, as I was emotionally care-free for the first time in many months. I am at peace and it feels really good. We get to the parking lot, and it dawns on me: my car is at work.

"Shit!"

"Your car is at your office."

"Yep, shit. No problem, we can call a cab."

"Or we can walk?"

"Is it okay if we don't? I don't want to walk that far. My feet are sore, and I really want to enjoy today with you. It's over ten miles away. We'll take the cab to my car, and then we'll go eat. Good?"

"That sounds like fun. Can I sit in the front seat with you? The only car I have ever been in was a police car, and they made me ride in the back, and the windows didn't open – actually, neither did the doors. I think they were broken."

"Yeah, broken. We'll have to walk a few blocks to where the cabs run near Main."

"Great, a little walking, my favorite, and a car ride for you."

We set off, and when you walk with God, you keep your eyes open, so when I notice a lot of people just standing on Main Street, I get really concerned. Within a block of the crowds I was happily relieved to find they are gathered for the Memorial Day parade. The day just got better. Until last night, parades, holidays, Sundays, like today - heck any reminder of happiness - were poison to me because my baby was always in those memories. We were inseparable and, oddly, we still are today. I whisper to myself.

"Hey baby. Good morning. I love you."

I know she can hear me now. Well I think she can. Wow! Cool either way, it makes me feel good. Life is quickly becoming better now. God is pumped for the crowd and the parade. I explain that this is right up his alley. It is a parade to celebrate the people killed in a war. It is about showing love to people who have passed protecting the country.

280

"And it's a celebration? I guess if you could stop warring that would make for a real big parade, instead of trying to remember the dead family members with photos and signs, grave markers, and flags, you could just turn around and give them a hug and tell them how much you love them. Ya'll will figure it out one of these centuries."

Well, I guess God's got a point - as always. But he is still chipper and excited for the parade that has just begun. The sidewalks are filled with people, three deep. Smaller children are sitting on the curb at the feet of their parents. We blend into the crowd on the sidewalk. The sun is warming the mid-morning sky. The flannel shirt I am wearing looks way out of place in this heat. I roll up the sleeves and unbutton a few buttons, but this offers little relief. It is really getting hot out.

The police chief and fire chief, lead the parade with their children riding on the top of a hook and ladder truck. Then one band after another, with clowns on unicycles, mounted police, soldiers dressed in fatigues to dress blues, march to the delight of the crowd. There are retired vets, a few floats from local businesses - all baking in the mid-morning sun.

Shit. Just as I was about let down my rolling - with God guard, walking up the same parade route, but a little closer to the right-side curb is a homeless and clearly mentally handicapped woman, dragging, yes, dragging, a shopping cart missing two wheels: the front left and the back right. It was full of, I think, recyclables: some cans and what looks like blankets and garbage. The most noticeable contents were two huge pieces of wood, possibly planks from a grand-stand at an athletic field. They are attached in the middle, with some sort metal hinge holding them together. They are each eight feet long, unwieldy for even a strong, sane man. The wood was so long that the ends drag on the street out the back, and if she didn't balance the cart on two wheels just right, and she couldn't, this horrible scrapping noise sends a nails-on-a-chalk-board shriek, so odd and loud it cuts through the parade noises. So much for an uneventful parade.

Most of the adults don't even look at her, and the kids, seeing her, throw hard candy at her; the same candy that they

281

received from passing clowns. When she is pelted and sees that it is food, she quickly eats a piece and starts crawling on the street trying to pick up as many pieces as possible. When the kids see this they start throwing more candy and other refreshments brought by their parents at her and laughing. Fuck! I turn to God to check his temperature; maybe he doesn't even see it.

I spin to my right side, where he is standing and is now gone. Spin to my left where the woman is coming up the street, and God has already gotten to her, and is helping her off her knees. He begins picking up some candy for her. Rude teens and kids mock him and keep tossing candy, now cups, trash, anything loose they can find. Shit! He turns his back to the crowd and begins again to help the woman with her cart and belongings. Now candy and garbage are flying in from all directions. Are they shitting me? That's fucking it! I rush the 42 feet to where this is playing out and get between the crowd, God, and the woman.

"Stop it! What kind of people are you?"

The projectiles stop flying. The culprits melt back into the crowd: some run, some just put their heads down. I turn my focus to the woman and God.

"Everybody okay?"

God is still in great spirits.

"We're fine aren't we sweetie?"

"Candy!"

The woman is not in touch with reality.

"Yes she is. She just can't go from here to here well."

God points to his forehead then to his mouth.

"Where are you going, honey?"

She points down the street and, of course, it is right along the path of the parade. Figures.

"Well, we better get going."

God grabs the two large pieces of wood and slings them over his shoulder, dragging the longest piece on the pavement behind him. I'm in charge of the cart with the two wheels. Shit, I don't know how she managed to get this far. I wish I had the planks. I start forward with God and the woman. She is nervous about us helping her. She begins to cling to the cart, and I struggle to push it with her hanging onto the side of it. The two broken wheels aren't helping.

Looking at her, she was every bit of five feet nothing and maybe 90 pounds, so I pick her up and put her in the cart's front seat as you would a child. She enjoys the lift and her new perch. We are off and now part of the parade; she is giggling with excitement.

God drags the beams down the street; my homeless passenger in the cart cheers our efforts and is screaming.

"Candy!"

We are quite a sight. A woman who has been watching the entire melodrama with the candy play out sees God stopping to adjust the boards over his shoulder and walks up to him and offers him a sip of her water from a plastic bottle and then walks along-side him as she sifts through her purse until she finds a handy wipe, sanitized packet, that she tears open and wipes the sweat that was falling into his eyes from his brow. He grabs her hand and puts the God wiggle on her. She runs back to her husband on the sidewalk and gives him a huge hug and kisses. A quickie, I guess. After another 60 feet, a fat man comes out and picks up the dragging end of the wood plank and walks along with God.

I've got to tell you the difference in watching a crowd become hostile toward a handicapped, homeless woman, and what God brings out in these people is the difference between love and hate. It is truly love, the power of the universe and this guy wields it as quick as it takes a broken heart to beat. Within a couple hundred feet and ten minutes, the crowd is now coming up to the cart and delivering cold bottles of water, food, candy - anything and everything they brought to the parade.

A teenage boy drops in some trail mix and walks flanking the cart and holds up the front end of the cart missing the wheel. God, carrying the large beams, looks back and smiles at the outpouring of affection. He starts thanking everyone in the crowd. His thanks motivate people to continue their donations into the cart. I look over the woman's shoulder and into the cart. I see, in addition to food and drinks; money - and a lot of it. There has to be $100 in bills in here!

The woman, laughing, smiling, and crying, holds her hands to her mouth in unbridled joy and adulation. She screams in inaudible tone that I think is "thank you" over and over to everyone. She is now crying and waving to everyone.

And wouldn't you know it, the most watched entry into the parade, getting the biggest applause, is not the bands, the clowns, fire trucks, mayor, or police chief, but God, his wooden beams, leading the homeless woman in the cart stocked with goodies for a year, and your humble, happy, servant pushing her. We were quite a sight.

We make a slight turn where the street chicanes and I find us at the end of the parade route. I am glad; I can tell God is tired. The parade ends at city hall where a portable stage has been erected. I guess there are festivities. The city hall building is a grand old building with a clock tower and steeple. God sets the woman, her cart full of goodies, her large wooden planks - I assume to build a lean-two at night with the blue plastic at the bottom of her cart - neatly under a shady tree. She is very excited. It's been a big day for her. After God delivers all her belongings, he walks over to the woman and hugs her for probably ten whole seconds. When He breaks the embrace, she looks Him right in the eye and with crystal clear queen's English she says;

"Thank you. It has been so long since anyone helped me."

"You're welcome. Go find your children and have a great day!"

She puts her face in her hands and begins to cry. Fuckin'
A; what *can't* this guy do? I thought she was mentally challenged.
She was just broken - and my boy fixed her.

Everyone is milling around looking to get a good view of
the stage on the steps of city hall. American flags are everywhere.
It is a glorious day and God seems to be really enjoying Himself,
watching families with strollers loaded with kids with cotton
candy faces, positioning themselves for the best vantage point.
Dads hoisting kids up on shoulders, moms holding babies, and
kids chasing balloons in the sea of love, and there is God smiling
from ear to dirty ear. It was life, love in all God's hopeful glory.

City hall sits in front of a grassy square with streets on all
four sides, a roundabout you would more likely find in Europe,
but today the traffic was redirected away from the area so people
could walk the streets and mill about. We take our position in the
dead center of the square next to the focal point; a statue of the
first mayor of the town: Ferris Gestas Dismas. The story goes that
he emptied the city's coffers and died in the bed of a prostitute
before he was indicted. Preservationists believed that even though
he may not be the beacon of leadership, he was still the first
mayor - so his likeness stays. I actually believe they probably had
no one better over the years to put there or else couldn't find the
money to switch the statue out.

As the program is about to start, noon chimes from the
clock in the steeple begin to ring. The bells sound crystal clear and
glorious; the perfect soundtrack for the day. And since it was
noon we enjoy 12 loud cycles of four bells.

Everyone's attention is drawn back to the stage when a
loud bellow of microphone feedback blares and rattles the
speakers set up around the area. It does grab everyone's attention
and the sound blast acts like a theater's house lights flashing,

alerting everyone that the show is about to start. The crowd settles as the military memorial service hosted by the VFW begins.

The mayor welcomes everyone, and then a priest gives a blessing to all in the crowd and asks us all to remember the fallen soldiers. I glance at God as he listens to the priest. He smiles and rolls his eyes like it was bullshit. The next speaker is a retired Navy veteran dressed in a blue and gold uniform with a Aussie Digger hat, a white plume arches from the side and flows off the back. He had to be 85 years old and, as I learn from another old salt standing next to me with the same hat, they are an organization of retired submarine sailors from World War II; a dying breed of some of the nation's greatest fighters in the Pacific and Atlantic theaters.

The submarine vet at the microphone speaks of loss and sacrifice. You can tell he is really proud and really moved. It touches everyone in the crowd. Everyone bows their heads, and the old sailor begins to ring a bell, 52 times, the number of submarines that were sunk in World War II. He said a few prayers with one ending with; all sailors who have passed should now rest in the arms of God. When he said that, God turns to me and says;

"They are. They are having fun now."

I know he digs it. I smile and God smiles back warmly. Then another odd God moment.

"I love you. Love everyone. Take care."

"Huh? What?"

38

Oh my God! Oh my God! You really are bleeding!
Stop it! You can stop it!
You can do anything! Fucking stop it!

God turns back to watch the pageant. That seems out of place even for God. After the old sailor leaves the stage seven marines in dress blues march to the side of the stage with parade rifles for, I assume, a 21 gun salute. I hear another Marine count out a cadence, sending the seven men into action. The first shots rang out, and everyone winces a little, then the second. I'm glued to the activity.

In between the second shots, and awaiting for the third, I hear other loud cracks in the distance. I now know this sound. Three more cracks. As I swing my body to the left, I feel this pain of being punched or hit with a baseball bat in right bicep. I grab my right arm with my left hand. Blood pumps and oozes out between my fingers. I fall to my knees. I am mortified! I turn to God for help.

"I BEEN SHO-! Oh Fuck! Oh you mother fuckers!""

God is lying on the ground, cracks one and two hit him in the chest, and the third hit me then grazed his neck. He is bleeding out quarts. I cannot feel or move my right arm, but I throw myself on him.

The crowd screams hysterically and scrambles; chaos ensues. My focus is no longer my arm but God. Fuck! Fuck! Fuck! They are going to kill him right here! Fucking right here? Right now? Fuck! Fuck! Fuck! I am lying on top of his chest. He looks at me, mouth full of blood pumping up through his throat. He smiles. Through a horrible gargling voice, he says,

"Get me up!"

Good thinking. I will firemen's carry his ass to safety.

"I'll get you out of here! SOMEONE HELP ME! Do you know who this is? Please, PLEASE, someone help!"

No one is paying attention to us. Everyone is running in all directions, grabbing loved ones and running, or hitting the deck. There are no kids on shoulders right now. Bullets sizzle past us. I scramble with one bad arm to get God to his feet. He is already ashen. He gestures me to take him over to the nearby statue of the first mayor. I figure he is trying to find cover. I drag him to the side of the base of the statue and lean him against the wall.

"Oh my God! Oh my God! You really are bleeding. Stop it! You can stop it! You can do anything! Fucking stop it! "

The fatherly smile never leaves his face. He forces words through coughing and vomiting blood, huge amounts of blood. He grabs me by the front of my shirt and pulls me toward his mouth. Another round ricochets near our heads.

"Love! Love life! Enjoy the love of the universe. I am there. She is there. Love people. Love everyone. Love by example. You are not alone any longer. "

"I love you. I know I feel you here."

I touch my heart. I'm losing it. My eyes well with tears.

"I do love you. I truly do! I NEED SOME FUCKING HELP OVER HERE! Stay with me! SOMEONE CALL 911! DO YOU KNOW WHO THIS IS?"

God shakes his head no.

"Get me up."

"No! Stay down! Help is coming!"

"Get... me.... up... please!"

"No! Fucking stay still, please!

> He won't have it. He wants to be up. With all my power, mostly from my left arm, I pull him up to a standing position in a gallon of his spilled blood. A bullet hits an elderly woman lying a few feet from us. There is blood everywhere. I have never seen so much blood. God asks me to help him up on the first level of the statue, which will elevate him above the screaming crowd. Does he want to try to calm everyone? But if I help him up, he is again, an easy and accessible target.

"Please! Hurry!

> He is losing consciousness, becoming grayer, and struggles to hold his eyes open and forward. His head slumps. I feel him grab my shoulder to try to carry his own weight.

"Hurry!"

> I lift his right foot up onto the step and push him forward to elevate him to the stoop.

"I... can... end... this... Hur...ry!"

> End this? I push his butt up with my shoulder. He is now standing two feet above the hysteria and chaos. Bullets whiz past us. What can he say now to quell this madness? But I've seen him do so many things he will not surprise me if he can. I just

don't know how. With his left hand he waves me down to take cover.

"What? I'm coming up there, too?"

He shoots me a stern look and waves me down, this time more urgently. Bullets riddle the statue. I curl back below the stoop, crooking my body so I can watch whatever he is planning. With whatever energy he has left he takes the last step he will ever take in that woman's gym shoe. He hoists himself up to the top level. He now stands next to the mayor's statue. He lists.

"God!"

He points at me to stay down with a mad look on his face to scare me. With any life, breath or strength he has left, he lifts his head, chin up, dignified with style, then opens his eyes. His Caribbean-blue eyes are crystal clear in the sun, a warm smile crosses his lips for the last time. God glances down and smiles at me and mouth the words, 'I love you, goodbye'. He smiles then raises his arms out parallel to the ground.

"What the fuck are you DOING?"

Too late! A gun shot tears his right hand from his arm. Bone, cartilage, blood and flesh splash all over my face.

"GOD!"

He shakes his head for me not to move. He elevates his right arm missing the hand, again both arms parallel to the ground. The next shots come almost on top of each other, the first wings his brow. Blood pours from his scalp line. His head rocks back then down to the left. He begins to stumble. The second catches his left side under the rib-cage, and I watch chunks of his body cavity blast through the back of his flannel shirt in a burst of red blood and smoke. The force blows him off the perch. He is falling backward. I stand, cradle out my arms, and catch God, but his weight and my bad arm have no chance of stopping us from crashing to the pavement. He lands on top of me. I quickly roll him over so he is lying on his back in a pool of his own blood.

"NO! YOU MOTHER FUCKERS!"

I begin to cry uncontrollably.

"Why did you do that? I need you. I can't do this without you, Goddamn you! HELP ME!"

He is fading in and out of consciousness. His breath is shallow. I try to stop the bleeding by putting my hand on his heart.

"SOMEONE HELP ME! SOMEONE CALL 911! HEEELLLLLLPPPP! FUCK!"

His eyes go cold. I try to shake Him awake.

"Come on! Goddamn you! YOU ARE GOD! Come on! You can do this! You can do anything! I've seen You do everything. You saved me! You showed me how to love! Now save Yourself! Goddammit!"

I pound His chest trying some pathetic attempt at CPR, but I am just pounding into bloody hamburger. I can't even feel His ribs, torn out by gun fire. I reach around His back and hold Him close like He has done to me so many times, teaching me how to love again, feel love, share love - but there is nothing left.

"Feel my love! Feel my energy! Come on! Try! I'm strong now! You made me strong! You showed me how to love again! Come on! Try! Try Goddammit! FUCK! "

His body slumps, muscles relax for the last time. He is gone. I pull Him close and bury my head in His shoulder. I wail uncontrollably. I can't take this anymore. I just don't want to let Him go. God, this is all getting way too familiar. Is love this hard? Why is pain so frequent in my life? And the blood! Oh, the fucking blood.

I squeeze His lifeless body tighter. No electricity. No whammy. I get nothing. I am a lost, brokenhearted, undeveloped mere mortal with no power of love racing through the universe. I am alone again with no power to save him. Not fucking me. Not now.

I cry like a baby for what seems like hours. I raise my head to find His bullet riddled, blood soaked face, cleaned by my tears and my shoulder pressing against it. I squeeze Him one more time, not for Him this time, but for me. You miss hugging people when you are alone. Surprisingly one of His lungs must not have been pierced and His last breath burps out, changing His expression to His warm enchanting smile. I smile back and hug Him one more time.

As I hold Him tight, His left arm slips from my embrace. His arm slumps to the ground, His hand hits the pavement, and oddly I hear a familiar pinging noise. I glance over His bloody shoulder and see His left hand on the pavement, fallen open. A few inches from His blood soaked, open hand is my wife's wedding ring. I pick it out of the pool of God's blood and put it in my mouth to clean it. I remove it from my mouth and just stare at it: shiny and sparkling, so her. My God's got skills even after He bails. I glance at Him with His loving smile on His gray, ashen face and at that moment I knew I was going to be okay.

He was right; he stopped the shooting. He saved everyone that day except for Himself. He gave Himself to the shooters to end the hysteria. His was the only fatality that day and everyone else was unhurt.

A fire fighter with medical gear comes up to the tangled, bloody heap of flesh that is our bodies. He asks me to let go so he can administer aid, but I know it is too late. This is the second person I love that died in my arms, and the third this weekend. The memory is and always will be haunting. They had to pry me from Him.

"Do you know this man?"

292

The fire fighter looks at me in the eyes and repeats himself.

"Do you know this man?"

"Yes."

"What's his name."

"It is God!"

"What?"

It's…it's… God."

I hear the fire fighter bark into his clip-on lapel microphone.

"We have two gunshot victims here, one dead, one wounded and in shock!"

"No I am not. I am not in shock. Nothing shocks me anymore. That *is* God."

"Sir don't move."

Now into the microphone:

"Stat on that second gunshot victim."

I lean against the base of the statue glancing back and forth from the blood soaked sheet covering up the creator of the universe and my wife's wedding ring. In time, a coroner's truck comes to remove God from the center of the park. I make an attempt to explain to the EMS people that this man is God. After two pathetic attempts, and in fear of ending up in the hospital psychiatric ward with my gunshot wound, I tell them I don't really know who the man is. They found no identification on him.

I never saw Him again.

293

I am being helped to an ambulance by a police officer. We are walking away, backs turned to the once festive parade route and town square. The police officer stops me just short of the ambulance, and he turns me round to look at the square in front of city hall, littered with folding chairs, abandoned strollers and coolers - the exact opposite of how it was 45 minutes ago. Circled around where God was killed are hundreds of people kneeling, most crying. I look up at the large police officer helping me. We stare into each other's eyes. It was the cop from the Denny's last night whose wife Marilyn had passed. He looks at me and smiles, never saying a word. He puts his arm around me and we walk the rest of the way to the ambulance. When I get there, he bear hugs me, nods, winks, then smiles goodbye.

EPOLOGUE

Your life changes when you spend a weekend with God.

Your life changes when you spend a weekend with God. Over the next three years I found balance in what I have learned and what I can see. I have mended and feel truly alive. I feel wonderful knowing my baby is happy and is in a much better place, awaiting my arrival. I am even more excited that occasionally when my mind is clear my dreams may really be her and me together. How cool is it to enjoy life knowing there is much *more* beyond this place, and how insane the real truth about the universe and how it all became and how it all works.

When I try to approach friends, religious people, scholars, scientists or even religious fanatics, they dismiss me as a loon, calling the information from God's lips, folly. I do not speak of my weekend to anyone. I thought I could actually change the world with God's love and knowledge, but what I have learned is that the world seems to only change one person at a time and that person this time is me.

The flat screen television has found a new home in my new house in the old neighborhood on a wall. I poured a glass of wine and finally opened the beer box with our photos. I spent an entire evening laughing and crying as I went through every one meticulously putting them back in order. What joy I had remembering the past and thinking about our future together.

The people that purchased our home are still there and have become great friends. They have me over as often as I care to be there. My attitude toward others and life have made me one of the most well-known, and popular people in the city. I want to enjoy my expanding universe. I make it a life requirement that I meet one new "friend" a day; more if possible. I also help out someone in need every day.

I share many of my meals with people less fortunate. I hug people now instead of shaking hands. I spend endless hours in the library reading about the heroes of the expanding universe. If I meet someone who is in trouble emotionally, financially, or any other way, I reach out to them and offer my assistance. I go to the hospital no fewer than three times per week - the hospital my wife died in - and talk to people about the strength of love and the love of an entire family, and how it is important to circle around people who are struggling with cancer and other diseases and draw their love and energy out to the person in need. I find myself standing outside hospital rooms and concentrating on what ails the person in there, hoping some of God's universal power and what little I have and, presently, helps the person.

When I go to sporting events I try to start waves and get crowds going to help my favorite players. My life is utter bliss, wrapped in the joy and love of many. I haven't married. With my wife in my life still and with the knowledge of joining her someday soon, there is just not enough room in my heart for two true loves. Without the assistance of Facebook or any on-line social media services - the internet doesn't give you the connection with people - I have over 1,958 people that I call friends: close friends that I spend hours with them - and their extended families. I am blessed and rich in so many ways. My calendar is stocked with love and happiness. God would be very proud. I don't think I will command the energy to create a universe, but I sure can't wait to get in this one.

DATELINE: _Milwaukee, Wisconsin. A six-year-old girl was sent home from school yesterday. Administrators say that while painting in her first grade class, she fashioned a sign that read: TALK TO GOD! She then left class without permission and went to the principal's office where she began holding the sign up in front of the school's principal._

After a number of warnings the child persisted, at which time her parents were called and she was sent home indefinitely. That same evening the child had sneaked out of her home and walked to the home of the principal, over ten miles away, where police found her standing in her pajamas on the man's front lawn holding the same sign above her head.

If you remember, tragedy has crippled this same family just 6 months ago when his 14 year old daughter was raped and killed in this home while her parents were attending a movie. Regarding the girl, she was taken home and has been scheduled for psychological testing.

NEVER THE END